characters

celebrating childhood
story heroes

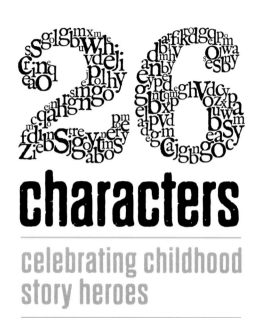

26
characters
celebrating childhood story heroes

Cambridge Jones & Alice Rochester

Foreword by Andy Stanton

New stories by Neill Cameron, Jamila Gavin,
Alex Kanefsky & Geraldine McCaughrean

Character icons by Robert Fresson

For Amber Emmanuelle and Sasha Lola – Cambridge Jones

For fictional characters everywhere – Alice Rochester

And with our special thanks to Ginny

First published in Great Britain in 2014 by
The Story Museum
Rochester House
42 Pembroke Street
Oxford OX1 1BP
www.storymuseum.org.uk

The Story Museum is a private not-for-profit company limited by guarantee,
no. 4780380. Registered charity no. 1107809

Sponsored by Arts Council England

10 9 8 7 6 5 4 3 2 1

A CIP catalogue record for this book is available from the British Library.

ISBN 978 0 9569918 1 2

Design & layout: Amanda Brookes at Brookes Forty
Project editor: Paul Forty at Brookes Forty
info@brookesforty.com

All reasonable efforts have been made to obtain requisite permissions and copyright
clearances. Any omissions and errors of attribution are unintentional and will, if
notified in writing to The Story Museum, be corrected in future printings.

Printed and bound in Great Britain by Pureprint. Pureprint is a CarbonNeutral company.

CONTENTS

FOREWORD
by Andy Stanton

Dear children of all ages,

Aren't stories amazing? Some of them have sharks in (e.g. *Jaws 2*) and some of them don't (e.g. *Noddy* – that would be horrible, wouldn't it?). Yes, stories are amazing. And to celebrate that fact, Cambridge Jones and the Story Museum have spent the last year or two throwing dresses and wigs and hats at various children's authors and making the camera go "click" at more or less the right time. The results are inspiring, joyful, silly, fantastical and sometimes downright terrifying.

All the people in this collection love stories and love reading. That is why they became authors. (That and the money, fast cars and dancing girls.) It is the Story Museum's fondest hope that, as you turn the pages of this book, your own passion for stories will be kindled, or rekindled. Perhaps you'll be encouraged to investigate a children's classic you haven't yet met. Or maybe you'll revisit one of your own favourite books and see it in a new light. Whatever, these photographs remind us that stories aren't one-off experiences. They're there to be picked up and played with over and over again. You're never too old. Or too young.

So. Enough from me. A treasure trove of freaks and weirdos awaits you. Goodies, baddies, meanies and in-betweenies. All your favourite characters! All your favourite authors! It's enough to make your eyes pop and your brains explode with happiness.

Aren't stories amazing?

Andy Stanton ☺

P.S. Meg Rosoff and I were photographed for this book too; but sadly the folks who hold the keys to our chosen characters wouldn't let them out to play. Take it from me, though – Meg looks really hot in a blue wig and bright red onesie.

PREFACE
by Cambridge Jones

Once upon a time, I lived in a land far, far away, called Oxford. (Though I used to call it Narnia because it felt very special and magical to me.)

While I was there I was approached and asked whether I'd like to work with a new museum that was going to bring stories and storytelling to life. The people seemed very charming and the building was huge and right in the centre of Oxford. The museum people said it would open in about two years and they were going to call it the Story Museum. They said that it would have magical elements and amazing things to see and do. I checked to see if their noses grew as they said this and they didn't, so I decided to believe in this extraordinary world they were talking about.

We decided to create an exhibition of the greatest storytellers. We concluded that just asking writers and storytellers to sit as my subjects was not sufficiently in keeping with the magic of the building and the big plans. So we decided to ask them all who their favourite character from childhood stories was… and then we would photograph them as that character.

The Royal Shakespeare Company and the National Theatre helped us, and we had a very talented make-up artist on every shoot.

The real beauty of the project was watching the writers inhabit and come to life as their chosen character. It was like watching a spirit take them over.

I then had the pleasure of sitting down and interviewing each and every one of our 26 characters (26 characters in the alphabet – see what we did there?), and that is when their stories really came to life, hearing about the role of stories in their childhoods, the authors and storytellers that excited them and the reasons they had decided to become storytellers themselves.

It was so engrossing and intoxicating, it could almost be a book in itself. Oh, wait… it is!

This work has turned into a journey of love and passion for me. I hope you enjoy it and find your own favourites among all the wonderful subjects. They have certainly inspired me.

INTRODUCTION
by Alice Rochester

66 'What is the use of a book,' " Alice famously observed, just before she tumbled into Wonderland, " 'without pictures or conversations?' "

This is a book of pictures and conversations, collected by the talented portrait photographer Cambridge Jones for the Story Museum's *26 Characters* exhibition. An exceptional array of authors kindly agreed to don wigs and eyepatches, face paint and peg legs, be photographed in various uncomfortable poses, and take part in these conversations. It has been a delightful process and we're hugely, eternally grateful to them all.

Many people helped behind the scenes and are acknowledged elsewhere. But one deserves special mention. We would especially like to thank Ginny Battcock for inspiring and supporting this project, organising and styling the photo shoots, and quietly helping to make the magic happen.

Some of this magic came from the special affection people hold for their favourite story characters. We quickly discovered that when you ask someone about their fictional friends the conversation lights up, and as soon as they name Samwise Gamgee or Eeyore, Pippi Longstocking or the Cat in the Hat, you learn something new and important about them. Our authors lit up more than most, and completely inhabited their chosen characters. Some could hardly be persuaded to take off their wigs and return to real life.

As well as pictures and conversations, this book contains extracts from the books that first introduced these much-loved characters and new versions of stories that began as oral tales. We're particularly grateful to Jamila Gavin and Geraldine McCaughrean for their original tellings and to Kevin Crossley-Holland for adapting a passage from his book *The Seeing Stone*.

We have also included background information about the authors and their favourite characters, and suggestions of where to look next if you'd like to get to know them even better. You can find more on the Story Museum's website (www.storymuseum.org.uk), including a digital gallery which allows you to create and share a picture of your own favourite character and become part of the conversation.

We hope Alice would approve.

bounced. There's no reason
t they made the rocks hum an
thing existed except the w
mother.
STO
a cut-
DRIP DRIP

26 characters

Malorie Blackman
THE WICKED WITCH OF THE WEST

" 'There is only one thing we can do,' returned
the Lion, 'and that is to go to the land of the Winkies,
seek out the Wicked Witch, and destroy her.'
'But suppose we cannot?' said the girl.
'Then I shall never have courage,' declared the Lion.
'And I shall never have brains,' added the Scarecrow.
'And I shall never have a heart,' spoke the Tin Woodman.
'And I shall never see Aunt Em and Uncle Henry,' said
Dorothy, beginning to cry."

One of the many fascinating components of this lovely job has been the response of my own children to the different authors I intermittently disappear off to create portraits with. Sometimes they appear unmoved by some of the greatest names in modern literature. Sometimes they work out days later that it was the author of one of their favourite books ("Daddy you could've told me you were photographing them!"), and sometimes it's Malorie Blackman ("OH MY GOD – YOU ARE PHOTOGRAPHING MALORIE BLACKMAN – CAN I COME?"). Well, no, they could not. Which is a shame, because we had such fun!

Cambridge Jones

WHO IS MALORIE BLACKMAN?

As a child, Malorie Blackman read everything she could lay her hands on. She had a vivid imagination and for two years carried a superhero costume around in her schoolbag, just in case. Malorie wanted to be an English teacher, but her careers adviser steered her into business studies, which led to computer programming. After a few years she took some time off to write and, 82 rejection letters later, published *Not So Stupid!*, a collection of short stories. Since then Malorie has written over 50 prize-winning books and picture books for children of all ages, as well as poems, plays and radio and TV dramas. She is best known for her *Noughts and Crosses* series, in which teenagers Callum and Sephy battle against a world divided by colour. Britain's Children's Laureate from 2013 to 2015, Malorie lives in London with her husband, daughter and 15,000 books.

Q & A

CAMBRIDGE JONES: So, who is your character, and why did you choose her?

MALORIE BLACKMAN: Well, my character is the Wicked Witch of the West from *The Wizard of Oz* and I chose her because I love baddies – and what would a good story be without a baddy? For each protagonist you need an antagonist. It's like for Harry Potter you need Voldemort, and in this case, for Dorothy you need the Wicked Witch of the West. The more powerful and the more evil the baddy is, then the stronger the heroine or the hero has to be to defeat them.

I remember the Wicked Witch of the West not just from the very famous film with Judy Garland but also from the book. In the novel, she has an eyepatch and she wears a silver whistle around her neck and she has a whole army of baddies that she sends after Dorothy. I loved reading about her as a child.

I learned to appreciate afterwards that all the women in the book were the ones with the power. Whether they used their power for good or ill, the women were real witches, and the Wizard of Oz was this charlatan. Everyone's looking up to him as the great and powerful wizard! In fact he's a fake. He just happened to land there in a hot air balloon.

What I loved was that Dorothy had power all the time in her silver shoes (they're ruby in the film but silver in the book) and she didn't know it. It's a very clever text, saying we women are stronger than we think.

CJ: Why do you think you became a storyteller?

MB: Well, it's because I love stories. I love thinking myself into new worlds, new situations, meeting new characters. There are so many wonderful stories out there and more to be told. I would read these stories and think, "Ooh, that's me in Narnia," or "That's me in Oz," putting myself in those situations and thinking, "What would I do?" It makes you empathise with other people. It gives you a brand-new way of looking at the world, and that's why I love being a writer. Some of my characters I might not necessarily like, so it's kind of interesting looking at the world through their eyes.

It's about trying to figure out what everybody wants, and then the story comes from when you try to stop them from getting it. In the Wicked Witch of the West's case she wants Dorothy out of the way. That's what I love about storytelling. You can do all kinds of things, and choose all kinds of baddies to act as obstacles in the way of what your main character wants.

I was always telling stories. As I was walking to school I was making up "what if" scenarios. What if I suddenly became invisible, what would I do? What if an alien came down and invited me back to their planet? Would I go? I was always a daydreamer. My teachers would say, "Malorie, get your head out of the clouds," as I would sit there making up all these stories in my head. It seems ironic that now that is how I make my living.

From the time I was seven or eight, I was always writing stories and poems for my own amusement. I was very lucky with my English teachers because they never said, "Stop wasting school paper." They would always just mark it and give me feedback. It never occurred to me until I was in my mid-twenties that maybe I could be an author and get myself published.

The Wonderful Wizard of Oz

by Lyman Frank Baum

THE STORY

A young girl called Dorothy is swept away from her dull life on the Kansas prairie by a cyclone. Her house lands in the magical Land of Oz, flattening the Wicked Witch of the East and releasing the tiny Munchkins she had enslaved. As a reward, Dorothy is given the Witch's magical silver shoes and advised that only the Great Wizard of Oz who lives in Emerald City can help her return home. As she travels along the yellow brick road, Dorothy befriends a scarecrow who wants a brain, a tin man who wants a heart and a cowardly lion. They all decide to ask for the Wizard's help. In Emerald City, Dorothy is told that to go home she must first defeat the Wizard's greatest foe, the Wicked Witch of the West. But the Witch is served by fierce wolves, evil crows, vicious bees, spear-wielding Winkie slaves and a pack of Winged Monkeys...

✳ ✳ ✳

The Wonderful Wizard of Oz, published in 1900, was written by Lyman Frank Baum and lavishly illustrated by W. W. Denslow. Baum, the sickly seventh child of a wealthy American businessman, tried breeding poultry, selling fireworks and running a theatre, shop and newspaper before he found success with books of nonsense poetry based on rhymes invented for his four sons.

Like Lewis Carroll, Baum believed in the value of fantasy and illustrations for children and set out to create stories with the wonder but without the violence and moralising of traditional tales. *The Wizard of Oz* became an international bestseller and inspired many comics, plays, musicals and films, most famously the 1939 movie starring Judy Garland. Encouraged by letters from thousands of children, Baum wrote thirteen sequels as well as many less successful fantasy novels, short stories, plays, films and poems. He remains a controversial figure, criticised for his views on native Americans, but admired for his strong female characters.

WHO IS THE WICKED WITCH OF THE WEST?

The Wicked Witch of the West is an evil tyrant with one powerful eye, a silver whistle that commands her wolves, crows and bees, and a golden cap that can summon the Winged Monkeys to destroy her foes. She covets Dorothy's silver slippers and traps her to gain their magical power. Dorothy throws a bucket of water over the Witch who, to her surprise, melts away. In the book the Witch carries an umbrella, but more people remember the 1939 movie character played by Margaret Howard – with green skin, pointed hat and broomstick.

> " Now the Wicked Witch of the West had but one eye, yet that was as powerful as a telescope, and could see everywhere. So, as she sat in the door of her castle, she happened to look around and saw Dorothy lying asleep, with her friends all about her. They were a long distance off, but the Wicked Witch was angry to find them in her country; so she blew upon a silver whistle that hung around her neck.
>
> At once there came running to her from all directions a pack of great wolves. They had long legs and fierce eyes and sharp teeth.
>
> 'Go to those people,' said the Witch, 'and tear them to pieces.'
>
> 'Are you not going to make them your slaves?' asked the leader of the wolves.
>
> 'No,' she answered, 'one is of tin, and one of straw; one is a girl and another a Lion. None of them is fit to work, so you may tear them into small pieces.' "

From *The Wonderful Wizard of Oz*, Chapter 12

Steven Butler
THE HATTER

Francesca Simon
THE QUEEN OF HEARTS

> "The Queen turned crimson with fury, and, after glaring at her for a moment like a wild beast, screamed, 'Off with her head!'"

> "'I want a clean cup,' interrupted the Hatter: 'let's all move one place on.'"

I drove Francesca and Steven from London to Oxford for the shoot. That turned out to be a good thing, because by the time we got there, there wasn't much we didn't know about each other and even less we were not prepared to do in front of each other. Which – when you are planning to photograph the Queen of Hearts and the Mad Hatter – is incredibly helpful. They were impeccable, and inspired, and fun, and spontaneous, and – well, just great. Steven was about to hand in his latest book to his publisher and had been on stage until late the night before, and Francesca… I was just so struck by her beauty when she lifted her hair and put on the robes. Stunning.
Cambridge Jones

WHO IS STEVEN BUTLER?

Steven Butler grew up in a tiny village in Kent, where his primary school headmaster was children's book author Jeremy Strong. At first Steven wanted to be an inventor, but when he left school he became an actor, dancer and circus performer, spending two years working on a Disney cruise liner. He went on to star in *Peter Pan*, *Joseph and the Amazing Technicolor Dreamcoat* and *Horrid Henry: Live and Horrid*, which is how he met Francesca Simon. It was while joking with Francesca that he must have been swapped at birth by trolls that his *Wrong Pong* series was born.

WHO IS FRANCESCA SIMON?

Francesca Simon was born in Missouri and grew up in California, where her father worked as a screenwriter. She attended Yale and Oxford universities, where she specialised in medieval studies, then spent several years working as a journalist in London. After her son was born she started writing children's stories full time. She has published over 50 books, including her prize-winning *Horrid Henry* series, which has sold over 20 million copies in 27 countries. Her books for older children include *The Sleeping Army* and *The Lost Gods*.

Q & A

CAMBRIDGE JONES: So who are your characters, and why did you choose them?

FRANCESCA SIMON: I am the incredibly glamorous Queen of Hearts and I chose her because I've always loved the idea of this crazed woman running around shrieking "Off with their heads! Off with their heads!" I loved that as a kid and, having reread it, I love it even more now because there's something kind of demented and passionate and completely self-obsessed about the Queen. And I do love characters like Lady Catherine de Bourgh in *Pride and Prejudice* that are completely oblivious to everyone around them and so rude. And so it's just a real chance to embrace my inner dictator!

I very much identify with the Rabbit, who is always looking at his watch, thinking, "Oh my god! I'm late! I'm late!" as that is very much me, anxious. I'm probably more like the Rabbit. But the Queen – she doesn't care what anybody else thinks, and I'm very drawn to characters who do not care

what anyone else thinks about them. She has this sense of total power and it's her world and she's going to do whatever she likes, which is the fantasy.

STEVEN BUTLER: I am the Mad Hatter. My first experience of *Alice in Wonderland* was the Disney film. I think they ruined it, but I was a real weirdo when I was growing up in my tiny little village, so zany characters really appealed to me. And so it was rather an obvious choice. We are paired together and we're friends and so instantly I was like, "Yep! Mad Hatter! Yes, yes, yes!" That scene, the Mad Hatter's tea party, even as a child, was a scene I always remembered. I was this little eccentric child and I always liked the Mad Hatter and the fact that it was rather brilliant to be absolutely insane, and for the first time the child is the sane one and the adult insane. I really liked that.

FS: The anarchy of it is great. All the characters are also very much passionately themselves. They just are who they are.

They never apologise. There's no explanation. They just drop in and they inhabit their own world and their own selves. It's incredibly appealing for a child.

CJ: What led you to write, to be a storyteller?

SB: I was very unhappy at school when I was a little boy because I was so different to everybody else, and I realised quite early on that I could lie enormously and people would just believe you. And so I started lying to anyone who was stupid enough to believe me and I could say ridiculous things. So I guess that was my initiation into storytelling. I was terrible at reading and got interested in books very late in primary school, right before secondary school. I started seriously writing probably in my mid to late teens. It was rubbish, but ten out of ten for effort.

FS: I don't consider myself a storyteller in that I can't make up stories on the spot. I consider myself a writer. I come up with lots and lots of ideas and I need to spend time developing them and thinking about them and seeing how they can work, and that takes me a long time, because I write fast but it takes me a long time to think. So I'm not quick in the sense of coming up with an imaginative story, but I'm quite patient in developing a story and nurturing it and combining strange things. I like that collision of ideas that shouldn't work and seeing if you could make them work.

I've always been a really keen reader, and my dad is a screenwriter and a playwright. So I grew up in a household where people were quite comfortable with words, where it seemed like a normal thing to do to write. I started writing when I was about eight or nine, little fairy tales and stuff. I didn't write very good fairy tales. It wasn't until my son was born and we started reading books together that I realised I had a complete knack. This was where I belonged, writing for children. It played to all my strengths. To write for children I think you need to be funny, you need to be logical, you need to be inventive, you need to have a kind of wild spirit. Writing for children is endlessly imaginative and fun.

Horrid Henry is a very subversive character, very much in the tradition of subversive characters. Of course Horrid Henry is the Queen of Hearts! He has so many of her qualities. He has that feeling that everyone has inside them, of wanting to be disruptive, of wanting to run around this room and break everything in it, of wanting to run screaming down the hall. And Peter is the more repressed side. So it's that balance between those two that really, really interests and excites me. I'm not interested in traditional stories. I hate stories that have morals. I hate when they're trying to teach things. I like much more left-field stories.

The other thing I like about writing children's books: I had a young child and I think had ten hours a week that I could actually write in. Because I was tired I could only keep small ideas in my head. So, I just got lots of ideas and started

writing all the time and it took me over a year to get published. I still remember the day that my first book was accepted, which was an amazing day because then I thought, I'm a writer. I am actually a writer. I'm not a crazed mother who thinks she can write.

It was actually the second book I wrote, which was called *Papa Forgot*. The parents have given very detailed instructions to the grandfather about how he is to look after this child and he ignores everything. They dance, they play, they have fun, and they have this amazing time. So I, very rule-bound, always put the character who breaks the rules as having this wonderful time. I love those kind of stories.

CJ: Do you interact with each other on the writing process?

SB: Oh god, yes! I'm handing in a book tomorrow, I literally just ran round with the manuscript and went, "Just have a read, is it good?" and thankfully it was.

FS: There were no red marks on it anywhere! And Steven is my first reader. Definitely. If I'm stuck on something, Steven will come over and I'll say, "Can I just talk you through this plot?" and Steven will get a notebook out. I had to do a battle scene, not my normal thing. He said, "Let's just write sentences down. We'll just throw sentences at each other." You know, "The giant picked up the bus and hurled it." We wrote about six or seven pages of sentences and then I spent the next two weeks putting it all together, but it really works. Steven really likes description, which I'm nervous about, and he has this great energy that I really enjoy, and he's fearless. We became friends before Steven had admitted to me that he wanted to write.

SB: We met because I played Horrid Henry and I was writing and I remember swearing to myself that I would never say anything to you.

FS: I remember his face when I said, "Do you want to write? Are you interested in writing?" and he almost seized up. There was something about the way he was asking me, the level of interest in his face was much more than the normal interest you might have in the way a writer works, so that's been a great bonus. Steven is the writer I actually trust the most in the world in terms of advice, in terms of reading something and telling me where I'm going right, telling me where I'm going wrong. In terms of working out ideas he's amazing. I really like the way Steven's writing reflects him as a person. It just has that edgy, impish, energetic, violent streak to it that I find really compelling and very funny.

SB: I like to laugh and I find your books are very funny, which is good. It's slightly weirder for me, because when I met you, you were already a hugely famous, very successful writer. Ultimately, your greatest quality is just that you're a really good writer. You're very funny and also I think your sense of humour has that streak of violence through it. I was a child of the Roald Dahl generation so I kind of grew up on violent humour, so that's what I find funny.

Alice's Adventures in Wonderland

by Lewis Carroll

THE STORY

One hot afternoon Alice is daydreaming on the riverbank. When a white rabbit wearing a waistcoat hurries by, checking his pocket watch and tutting about the time, she decides to follow, tumbling down a rabbit hole into a topsy-turvy world where it's always teatime, there are no rules, and a bad-tempered Queen wants to chop off her head...

✳   ✳   ✳

On 4 July 1862, Charles Dodgson, a mathematics don at Oxford University, took the ten-year-old Alice Liddell and her sisters on a rowing boat up the River Thames. To entertain them, he made up a story about a little girl who falls into Wonderland and has a series of strange adventures. The tale so delighted Alice that she begged him to write it down. The result was *Alice's Adventures in Wonderland*, which was published in 1865 under the pen name Lewis Carroll, with illustrations by the political cartoonist John Tenniel. It became one of the most popular and influential children's books ever written, and is still enjoyed – and studied – nearly 150 years later for its many layers of playfulness and invention.

" 'Herald, read the accusation!' said the King.

On this the White Rabbit blew three blasts on the trumpet, and then unrolled the parchment scroll, and read as follows:-

'The Queen of Hearts, she made some tarts, All on a summer day: The Knave of Hearts, he stole those tarts, And took them quite away!'

'Consider your verdict,' the King said to the jury.

'Not yet, not yet!' the Rabbit hastily interrupted. 'There's a great deal to come before that!'

'Call the first witness,' said the King; and the White Rabbit blew three blasts on the trumpet, and called out, 'First witness!'

The first witness was the Hatter. He came in with a teacup in one hand and a piece of bread-and-butter in the other. 'I beg pardon, your Majesty,' he began, 'for bringing these in: but I hadn't quite finished my tea when I was sent for.'

'You ought to have finished,' said the King. 'When did you begin?'

The Hatter looked at the March Hare, who had followed him into the court, arm-in-arm with the Dormouse.

'Fourteenth of March, I think it was,' he said.

'Fifteenth,' said the March Hare.

'Sixteenth,' added the Dormouse.

'Write that down,' the King said to the jury, and the jury eagerly wrote down all three dates on their slates, and then added them up, and reduced the answer to shillings and pence.

'Take off your hat,' the King said to the Hatter.

'It isn't mine,' said the Hatter.

'Stolen!' the King exclaimed, turning to the jury, who instantly made a memorandum of the fact.

'I keep them to sell,' the Hatter added as an explanation; 'I've none of my own. I'm a hatter.'

Here the Queen put on her spectacles, and began staring at the Hatter, who turned pale and fidgeted.

'Give your evidence,' said the King; 'and don't be nervous, or I'll have you executed on the spot.'

This did not seem to encourage the witness at all: he kept shifting from one foot to the other, looking uneasily at the Queen, and in his confusion he bit a large piece out of his teacup instead of the bread-and-butter."

From *Alice's Adventures in Wonderland*, Chapter 11, "Who Stole the Tarts?"

WHO IS THE QUEEN OF HEARTS?

The Queen of Hearts is one of the playing card characters in *Alice's Adventures in Wonderland*. She enjoys playing croquet with live flamingos as mallets and hedgehogs as balls. But it is vital that she wins, for if ever she does not get her own way she orders those around her to be beheaded. Alice later discovers that these threats are never actually carried out. The Queen of Hearts is sometimes confused with the Red Queen from the sequel, *Through the Looking-Glass*, who is a much colder, stricter monarch based on a chess character.

WHO IS THE HATTER?

We first meet the Hatter at the Mad Tea Party, where he is rude to Alice; then as a nervous witness at the trial of the Knave of Hearts. He is often known as the "Mad Hatter", although Lewis Carroll never called him this. The phrase "mad as a hatter" was common in Carroll's time, perhaps because hatters sometimes went insane from using poisonous mercury in hat-making. It is claimed that Tenniel's drawings of the Hatter are based on Theophilus Carter, an eccentric furniture dealer near Oxford, who always wore a top hat.

Cressida Cowell
PETER PAN

❝ 'So, Pan,' said Hook at last, 'this is all your doing.'
'Ay, James Hook,' came the stern answer, 'it is all my doing.'
'Proud and insolent youth,' said Hook, 'prepare to meet thy doom.'
'Dark and sinister man,' Peter answered, 'have at thee.' ❞

Cressida wanted to be Peter Pan. Lots of people wanted to be Peter Pan, in fact, but Cressida got there first. Cressida was more interested in the original character and drawings of Peter Pan than in the familiar cartoon or movie images. So we set about researching older pictures and managed to get the more earthy, rustic and impish Peter Pan that Cressida wanted, I think.
Cambridge Jones

WHO IS CRESSIDA COWELL?

Cressida Cowell grew up in London and on a small, uninhabited Scottish island. As a child she loved all forms of storytelling, and at eight began to write stories about Vikings and dragons. After reading English literature at Oxford University, she studied art and illustration, finding a commercial publisher for her final project, a children's book about Bo Peep, which launched her writing career. Since then she has written ten more picture books, including the Emily Brown stories, and eleven volumes of her very popular *Hiccup* series for older children. The first, *How to Train Your Dragon*, became a film in 2010.

Q & A

CAMBRIDGE JONES: What character have you chosen, and why?

CRESSIDA COWELL: My character is Peter Pan, and I chose him because it was a book that had huge importance for me when I was a child. It really resonated for me, partly because my childhood was split between London and a remote island off the west coast of Scotland. We would be dropped off on this island by a local fisherman and picked up again two weeks later. And there was *nothing* on that island. There were no houses. There was no electricity. There was no way of contacting the outside world if anything went wrong. So it was a bit like Neverland, this island that the Darling children went to. They grew up in London, but they went to this amazing island where anything was possible.

Peter Pan was also a book that inspired my *How to Train Your Dragon* books, which are also about growing up, about an island, about flying, and magic, and "are dragons possible?" in the same way as "are fairies possible?" So it was a very important book for me.

I wanted to be Peter Pan because he's this character with no responsibilities, who never grows up. The key for me was his cheek, and his bravery, and his refusal to be intimidated by Captain Hook, who was really quite scary. Peter Pan had that edge of darkness. We live in quite a safe world nowadays. I think that's one of the reasons that children are drawn to fantasy books, like mine, because they crave adventure and a world which could be dangerous but is *exciting*. And that is the heart of *Peter Pan* – the excitement, the danger, fighting with pirates, and being able to fly.

There's an extraordinary amount of children's literature in which the child is an orphan or is standing up against an adult world. Children spend their whole lives being told what to do, so the idea of a child who is outside all of that, who doesn't do what they're told, is immensely attractive.

CJ: And why did you become a storyteller?

CC: Even as a small kid I was a storyteller. From as soon as I could write I was writing stories. I was the eldest kid in my family, and I was telling stories to my brothers and sisters and cousins. And of course we were on this uninhabited island. As I grew older we were there for the whole summer, with no telly. So I was organising plays, reading aloud, telling stories and also drawing.

Even when I was at school I remember making up stories with other children. With one kid, we wrote each other letters when we should have been in lessons, pretending we were the mothers of these large families. And with another friend I wrote a romantic novel when I was about fifteen. So I suppose I was writing stories all through my school life.

I went into publishing first and I was *terrible*, because publishing is a business. I was *not* a business person. So I went to art school and that's where I began thinking I could do a creative job. I did think about going into the film business, into animation, telling stories in words and pictures, or eventually going down the book route.

Peter Pan

by J. M. Barrie

THE STORY

Peter Pan can fly and has decided never to grow up. He lives with his gang, the Lost Boys, on an island called Neverland, but returns to London sometimes to listen to stories outside the nursery window of the Darling children. One night he is seen, and loses his shadow as he escapes. When he returns for it, he wakes Wendy, the daughter, and discovers that she knows lots of stories. So he invites her and her younger brothers, John and Michael, to Neverland and teaches them to fly. The children soon find themselves caught up in dangerous adventures with mermaids and a fairy, pirates and a crocodile...

Peter Pan, the boy who wouldn't grow up, is the best-known creation of Scottish author and playwright James Matthew Barrie. Born in 1860, the ninth of ten children, Barrie's childhood was overshadowed by the death of an older brother, David, in a skating accident. Their mother comforted herself with the idea that he would remain a boy for ever.

After leaving Edinburgh University, Barrie worked as a journalist in Nottingham and then moved to London in 1885. There he began to publish novels, short stories and stage plays, and to make many friends including the Llewellyn Davies children, who inspired the story of Peter Pan and came to play an important, but often sad, part in Barrie's life. Peter Pan first appeared in *The Little White Bird*, an adult novel in which babies begin as birds. Barrie developed the story into a stage play, which was first performed in 1904. It was a huge hit in London and New York and appeared as a novel, *Peter and Wendy*, in 1911. After reports that children were hurting themselves jumping off beds and out of windows, Barrie later added the idea of needing fairy dust to fly. Peter Pan remains as popular as ever in books, animations, films, plays and games.

> " His sobs woke Wendy, and she sat up in bed. She was not alarmed to see a stranger crying on the nursery floor; she was only pleasantly interested.
> 'Boy,' she said courteously, 'why are you crying?'
> Peter could be exceedingly polite also, having learned the grand manner at fairy ceremonies, and he rose and bowed to her beautifully. She was much pleased, and bowed beautifully to him from the bed.
> 'What's your name?' he asked.
> 'Wendy Moira Angela Darling,' she replied with some satisfaction. 'What is your name?'
> 'Peter Pan.'
> She was already sure that he must be Peter, but it did seem a comparatively short name.
> 'Is that all?'
> 'Yes,' he said rather sharply. He felt for the first time that it was a shortish name.
> 'I'm so sorry,' said Wendy Moira Angela.
> 'It doesn't matter,' Peter gulped.
> She asked where he lived.
> 'Second to the right,' said Peter, 'and then straight on till morning.' "

From *Peter Pan*, Chapter Three, "Come away, come away!"

WHO IS PETER PAN?

Peter Pan is described as a beautiful boy "clad in skeleton leaves", but the rest is left to our imagination. Lost as a baby in Kensington Gardens, he flies to Neverland when he sees that his parents have had another child. Pan is a daring leader, skilled swordsman and clever mimic, inclined to boastfulness: "Oh, the cleverness of me." He fears nothing – except mothers and growing up – and claims that "death would be an awfully big adventure." His best friend is Tinker Bell, a fairy who protects him jealously.

Kevin Crossley-Holland
MERLIN

66 'Each of us needs a quest, and a person without one is lost to himself... I am Merlin the Magician and I know what you do not and see what you cannot. Nothing in the world is impossible, but there's always a price.' "

Mr Crossley-Holland, a gentle man and a gentleman. He had travelled far to be with us at the Story Museum for this shoot. Like a traveller of old he had stopped for the night en route for food, sustenance and a roof over his head. Imagine his surprise and mine when his hosts turned out to be great friends of us both. No ice-breaking required on this one!
Cambridge Jones

Kevin Crossley-Holland is a poet, novelist and scholar who is fascinated by the ancient languages and stories of Northern Europe. When he was small, his father, who studied early music, often told him old tales, accompanied by a Welsh harp. Growing up in the Buckinghamshire countryside, Kevin loved collecting archaeological treasures and set up a museum in his garden shed. At fourteen, he decided to become a priest, but changed his mind while studying English literature at Oxford University. There he became interested in Anglo-Saxon and, encouraged by J. R. R. Tolkien and the poet W. H. Auden, decided to translate *Beowulf*.

Kevin has travelled widely to research his stories. He has worked in Bavaria and he taught for five years in Minnesota, USA. He has written many novels, translations and collections of poetry and short stories, and enjoys setting words to music. He is best known for *The Seeing Stone*, a vivid retelling of the Arthurian legend, which won many prizes and has been widely translated.

Q & A

CAMBRIDGE JONES: Who is your character, and why did you choose him?

KEVIN CROSSLEY-HOLLAND: My character is Merlin. And Merlin is the arch-magician, the arch-wizard, the arch-enchanter of all British and European fiction. He is a seer and a prophet who tells the future. He can cast magic spells. He is a shape-changer. He is a guide who leads innocent people into darker, deeper paths: above all, Arthur, to become king of all Britain. He's the man who is responsible for Arthur being born at all. He moved the stones to Stonehenge from Ireland. He put the sword in the stone by which Arthur proves his kingship.

Sometimes, you cannot take your eyes off him when he's "on stage", because he's so fascinating. And you can't get him out of your head when he's off stage because you wonder what he's up to. He is the figure, the son of a spirit and a nun, who creates the whole world of Arthur that became so well known for several hundred years that every European language had its own Arthur stories. And since then there are Arthur sculptures, Arthur music, Arthur paintings. And so it goes on, and we each make our own new Merlin.

Merlin is not the first magician in world literature. But he's the one who had some historical roots in the sixth century. Merlin is not actually a first name or, as Christians would say, a "Christian name". A "merlin" is a "wise man". He was a wise man. Some people say he was mad. Some say he came from Strathclyde, or somewhere near Liverpool, or

Manchester; some say he came from the north of Wales. Wherever he came from, in a funny way he's everywhere. Because he stepped into our heads and hearts and will not go away.

CJ: What made you become a storyteller?

KC-H: I became a storyteller for three very simple reasons. My father used to sit by my bunk bed, I was on the top, my sister was on the bottom, with his Welsh harp, and he would sit and sing stories to us every night, including the story of a king who was asleep under a hill and would one day ride out and drive all those people we call Anglo-Saxons back into the North Sea from which they came. And I knew that he was asleep under the hill where I lived, not so far from here, and I always used to go searching for him.

Secondly, stories are what humans do. If I say, "Do you know? I had great difficulty in getting here this morning," I'm beginning to tell you a story. Stories are bits and bobs that we tell each other the whole time, which enclose our hopes and fears and longings and frustrations and terrors and joys and sharings and fightings and grievings. How would one not want to share this with other people?

And thirdly, I love language. I love the music of language. There's no great magic about being a decent writer: if you can make decent pictures with words and decent music with words, you're on your way to being a decent writer, because all humans can tell stories.

Merlin

THE RED DRAGON AND THE WHITE DRAGON

" 'You leaf-eaters!' Merlin exclaimed. 'Just look at all these holes, Arthur. Do you know how to get rid of caterpillars?'

'Merlin!' I said, 'I've got to talk to you.'

Merlin closed his eyes.

'The stone,' I began. 'The obsidian you gave me, its darkness cleared, and I could see a king – well, he was wearing a crown. He was sitting on a grassy bank, and below him a crowd of men were digging a pit. They were shovelling rocks and earth out of it. But then the pit filled with water.'

'And so the men drained the pit.'

'Do you know this story, then?'

'Tell me.'

'And when they'd drained it, I could see two caves. Two dark mouths. Out of one writhed a dragon with scales as white as lily spathe. Out of the other shrithed a dragon with scales as red as quick, fresh blood. They snarled, they threw spears of flame at each other. But who were they, Merlin? Why were they fighting?'

Merlin's eyes were still shut. He always closes them when he is listening carefully. 'Who won?' he asked me.

'I don't know. That's the trouble. My stone grew dark in my left hand again. Have you heard this story?'

'Questions!' he said. 'Questions! Now begin at the beginning, Arthur.'

'The king, then. Who was he?'

'What if I told you he was Vortigern?'

'Who? Where was his kingdom?'

'You see. The answer to that question only leads to more questions; and you have to know the answers to them as well before the first answer means anything. Vortigern was king of Britain.'

'When?'

'After those dratted Romans left us in peace. And before the Saxons broke that peace. Yes, Arthur, I've heard an old story that Vortigern wanted to build a tower, but when his men dug the foundations, there was a pool...'

'That's it!' I cried.

'Many questions,' said Merlin, 'are like nutshells – with their nuts still inside them. You've asked me about the dragons and why they were fighting. But haven't you heard of the red dragon of Wales and the white dragon of England? The Welsh and English have always been enemies, haven't they?'

'I see,' I said slowly.

'But you must see for yourself,' Merlin told me. 'It's right to listen to old stories, but what's the use of ancient knowledge? It's dry as dead leaves – no use, not even for caterpillars. No use at all unless you're ready for it.'

'I am ready,' I said."

Adapted from *The Seeing Stone* by Kevin Crossley-Holland, Orion Publishing Group, 2000

WHO IS MERLIN?

Merlin is a mythical character who has threaded his way through European legend and literature for nearly 900 years, shape-shifting as he goes. In about 1136, Geoffrey of Monmouth, a travelling scholar, combined the stories of a Welsh prophet, Myrddin, with those of the warrior Ambrosius to create Merlin Ambrosius, the son of a woman and an evil spirit, who can change shape and see into the past and future. Geoffrey's partly invented "history" of the earliest British kings tells of Merlin advising King Vortigern about two battling dragons and prophesying the rise and fall of King Arthur.

Geoffrey's manuscripts were copied and translated across Europe, and Merlin's story was embellished and retold down the years. He became a wild man, a wise man, a sorcerer, a young prophet, an old fool, a warrior, a priest and a bard. He became King Arthur's adviser, caught up in the search for the Holy Grail. He was bewitched by the Lady of the Lake, or by a huntress who turned his magic powers against him. Many versions end with him trapped in an enchanted prison – a tomb, cave, rock, tower or tree – but still he continues to hold us under his spell.

Ted & Pandora Dewan
POD & ARRIETTY

" 'Borrowing's a skilled job, an art like. Of all the families who've been in this house, there's only us left, and do you know for why? Because your father, Arrietty, is the best Borrower that's been known in these parts since – well, before your grandad's time.' "

Ted is as much a part of the Story Museum as anyone I have met during the two-year project to capture these images and create the exhibition. His was one of the first portraits we took, along with his daughter Pandora, and they chose *The Borrowers*. Ted went to great trouble (as he always does) to be creative with the props and detail, and we chose not to use trick photography or Photoshop to make them seem smaller. Just the essence of the characters and the props they had with them. I think that was the right decision, as Ted and Pandora seemed to me to capture the poignancy of the characters and their relationship. But I have a feeling that Ted (who is almost certainly a perfectionist) was less happy than me – so if you see him, tell him how wonderful they both look!

Cambridge Jones

WHO IS TED DEWAN?

Ted was born in Massachusetts, USA. He began drawing at the age of two (on the hall wallpaper), storytelling at three (about the fat boy who fell into some alphabet soup) and taking on paid commissions during his teens. He studied engineering and electronic music at university and spent five years as an unconventional physics teacher at a Boston boarding school before moving to London, where he worked as an illustrator and cartoonist and married children's picture book author Helen Cooper.

In 2001 they moved to Oxford and Ted divided his time between caring for their daughter Pandora, born in 1998, writing and illustrating picture books including *Bing Bunny* and *Crispin the Pig Who Had It All*, and bringing his distinctive brand of art and mischief to civic celebrations and traffic-calming schemes. Ted works in Philip Pullman's former writing shed and was the Story Museum's first artist-in-residence. Pandora shares her parents' creative talents and now has her own shed.

Q & A

CAMBRIDGE JONES: Who are your favourite characters, and why did you choose them?

TED DEWAN: Well, the Borrowers characters as an ensemble. I can do Pod because, when I think about it, I kind of live the life of Pod, in and out of skips, repurposing things. My daughter is Arrietty's age and the dynamic is really similar in that I'm trying to stick the wings on and realise that's she's able to assess danger on her own, and my wife is just that bit more cautious. Not as much a homebody and a claustrophobic presence as Homily, Arrietty's mom, but that dynamic is very familiar and I think it's quite classic with a family, especially with an only child.

I loved stories about people from other worlds. *The Borrowers* I liked simply because you had this separation between the Borrowers' world and the real world. I didn't like things that were too fantastic, because the suspension of disbelief was a lot more work. *The Borrowers* was such a well-realised bunch of stories, it was entirely feasible to see that not only could these people be living in the walls and under the floors, but that their concerns and their struggles for survival mirrored our own. I was just fascinated by it. The scale of them was just right.

CJ: Why do stories matter to you in your work and life?

TD: Well, in work, I'm in the story-making business. In life, I have had the privilege on several occasions of, in effect, brokering a true fairy tale, here in Oxford. There was a festival called Luminox, where we had this big fire installation. And that's something we originally got going years ago and then it built up. It was a proper story, and it had drama and it had heartbreaks and it had triumphs. And I really enjoyed seeing that story unfold before my eyes.

The storification of real life is a fascinating thing to try and do, because most of our lives don't have that nice narrative shape. But when you tweak people's perceptions of things, and you do the odd prank to make a particular moment in that story vivid, you then have before you the best story in the world. Because nobody knows how it's going to end. And that's easy to do in Oxford: nobody is more than two degrees of separation from anyone else, so stories kind of rip through it. You can play with this city like you couldn't a bigger one.

So, I'm looking at ways in which you can frame real events in real life into a narrative, hopefully leading to an interesting and happy ending. Of course real life doesn't always work like that. But there have been several occasions where real life becomes a story.

The Borrowers

by Mary Norton

THE STORY

Under the grandfather clock, below the wainscot, there is a hole where fourteen-year-old Arrietty Clock lives with her parents, Homily and Pod. The Clock family are Borrowers, tiny people who survive by borrowing items from the "human beans" who live in the house and do not even know they exist. One day, Pod comes home shaken: he has been seen by "the Boy" upstairs. Pod and Homily decide the time has come to teach their daughter to borrow safely. But on her first expedition Arrietty confides in the Boy, unwittingly putting the family in great danger...

The Borrowers are the creation of Mary Norton, who was born in 1903 and grew up in Leighton Buzzard, Bedfordshire, in the rambling Georgian house that appears in the story. After leaving art school, Mary worked as an actress before marrying and moving to Portugal, where she had four children. During the Second World War the family rented a house in Connecticut, USA, where Mary began writing children's books, publishing *The Magic Bed-Knob* in 1945. Its sequel became the Disney film *Bedknobs and Broomsticks*. *The Borrowers* was published in 1952, inspired by Mary's childhood fascination with tiny creatures, which she later attributed to her extreme short-sightedness. The book was hailed as a children's classic and has inspired several television series and films. *The Borrowers Avenged*, the fifth and final Borrowers story, was published in 1982.

WHO ARE POD AND ARRIETTY?

Borrowers are small and quiet, but heaven help anyone who thinks they might squish them. Borrowers think human beings were put here to provide what they need, "like bread is for butter". Not stealing, but borrowing. Pod Clock is a talented and ingenious Borrower, married to the careful Homily. Arrietty, their adventurous teenage daughter, must just read, write her diary, look up through the grating and dream, until her mother decides it is safe for her to venture upstairs.

"Pod came in slowly, his sack on his back: he leaned his hat-pin, with its dangling name-tape, against the wall and, on the middle of the kitchen table, he placed a doll's tea cup; it seemed the size of a mixing bowl.

'Why, Pod –' began Homily.

'Got the saucer too,' he said. He swung down the sack and untied the neck. 'Here you are,' he said, drawing out the saucer. 'Matches it.'

He had a round, currant-bunny sort of face; tonight it looked flabby.

'Oh, Pod,' said Homily, 'you do look queer. Are you all right?'

Pod sat down. 'I'm fair enough,' he said.

'You went up the curtain,' said Homily. 'Oh, Pod, you shouldn't have. It's shaken you –'

Pod made a strange face, his eyes swivelled round towards Arrietty. Homily stared at him, her mouth open, and then she turned. 'Come along, Arrietty,' she said briskly, 'you pop off to bed, now, like a good girl, and I'll bring you some supper.'

'Oh,' said Arrietty, 'can't I see the rest of the borrowings?'

'Your father's got nothing now. Only food. Off you pop to bed. You've seen the cup and saucer.'

Arrietty went into the sitting-room to put away her diary, and took some time fixing her candle on the upturned drawing-pin which served as a holder.

'Whatever are you doing?' grumbled Homily. 'Give it here. There. That's the way. Now off to bed and fold your clothes, mind.'

'Good night, papa,' said Arrietty, kissing his flat white cheek.

'Careful of the light,' he said mechanically, and watched her with his round eyes until she had closed the door.

'Now, Pod,' said Homily, when they were alone, 'tell me. What's the matter?'

Pod looked at her blankly. 'I been "seen",' he said."

From *The Borrowers*, Chapter 4

Julia & Malcolm Donaldson
THE OWL & THE PUSSY-CAT

"The Owl and the Pussy-cat went to sea
In a beautiful pea green boat,
They took some honey, and plenty of money,
Wrapped up in a five pound note.
The Owl looked up to the stars above,
And sang to a small guitar,
'O lovely Pussy! O Pussy my love,
What a beautiful Pussy you are,
You are,
You are!
What a beautiful Pussy you are!'"

To visit Julia and Malcolm at their home is a wonderful privilege. It is a little like being allowed into the wizard's cave. Not because you suddenly see a real live Gruffalo or a whale or snail, but because over time you start to sense the free and creative spirit that surrounds them and that they inhabit. Influences and inspiration are all around, and yet they remain so focused on the "story" they present, the entertainment, that everything feels like background to what they may do or say next. Which in my case was a lovely performance (with guitar) of the original "Owl and the Pussy-cat" and their new sequel. A treat of a day.

Cambridge Jones

WHO IS JULIA DONALDSON?

Julia Donaldson grew up in London and loved playing imaginary games with her sister, Mary. After studying Drama and French at Bristol University, she went travelling and busking with Malcolm, whom she later married. The busking led to folk-club performances and songwriting for children's television, and in 1993 the words of her song "A Squash and A Squeeze" were made into a book, the first of many illustrated by Axel Scheffler.

As well as continuing to write and perform songs, Julia has written nearly 200 books, including rhymes and stories for younger children, novels for older readers and teenagers, plays for schools, and a reading scheme called *Songbird Phonics*. She is best known for *The Gruffalo*, voted the nation's favourite bedtime story, which has sold over 10 million copies and appeared on stage and screen. While Children's Laureate (2011–2013), Julia campaigned to protect libraries, to promote books for and about deaf children, and to encourage children to perform stories, plays and poems. Malcolm Donaldson is a consultant and lecturer specialising in child health.

CAMBRIDGE JONES: Who is your character, and why did you choose it?

JULIA DONALDSON: My character is the Pussy-cat from Edward Lear's poem "The Owl and the Pussy-cat". I chose this character because I've always loved Lear's poetry, ever since my granny read it to me when I was a little girl. And actually Lear has influenced my own writing. In particular, my book *The Snail and the Whale* owes a lot to another of his poems, "The Jumblies", which is also about another voyage. And then of course, I am married to my own Owl — Malcolm plays the guitar, and acts the Owl in *The Gruffalo* when we perform that story on stage. So it just seemed a natural choice.

CJ: You say Lear influences the way that you write. Are you aware in what ways?

JD: I don't always write in verse, but when I do, Lear often seems to be looking over my shoulder. There's a lyrical, musical, sometimes even melancholy quality in his poetry, and I think I've maybe caught some of that, specially in *The Snail and the Whale* — the wistfulness perhaps, the yearning which creeps into Lear's writing. I've read that he could be quite a melancholy character himself, as well as being jovial and jolly much of the time.

I did start off as a songwriter, and although I don't exactly hear tunes in my head when I'm writing stories in verse I definitely have the rhythm strongly in my head and very often I later create a song version of my stories. In fact I have written a sequel to "The Owl and the Pussy-cat", and I did turn that into a song.

CJ: So why did you become a storyteller?

JD: I think why I became a storyteller — apart from the fact that I love stories, like loads of people — probably goes back to my student days when I went busking in Paris, with Malcolm, my Owl husband! We used to sing in the streets and take the hat round. That, in turn, led to me writing songs for children's television. And that led to one of my songs being turned into a book. And *that* led into me writing books. So in a way I've just done what I've been asked to do, but it's all ended up really well, because I'm really happy doing what I do.

I find it much harder to write stories than songs, because when you write a song you *don't* have to write a story, you don't have to work out the plot. If you write a song about horrible smells, which I did once, make a list of all the horrible smells you can think of, then choose the best ones and play around with them, making sure the very best one comes at the end as a kind of punchline — with a chorus about horrible smells in general! If you write a story about horrible smells, you would have to have someone who smells the horrible smells and something would have to happen to them. That's the bit that's so hard about being a writer, and that's the bit other people often don't think about. They say, "Where do you get your ideas?" and they forget it's not just about having an idea — you've got to develop that idea as a story. It's really important. It's got to go somewhere. It's got to have a climax. It's got to have a twist, and it shouldn't be just a string of coincidences.

The Owl and the Pussy-cat

by Edward Lear

THE STORY

"The Owl and the Pussy-cat" is a nonsense poem written by Edward Lear to entertain a friend's six-year-old daughter when she was ill. It was published in 1871 in his book *Nonsense Songs, Stories, Botany, and Alphabets* and contains one of Lear's many invented terms, "runcible spoon", which is now in the dictionary. The poem originally appeared with Lear's own illustrations, but has been re-illustrated many times, set to music and adapted as plays and animations. Beatrix Potter's *Little Pig Robinson* is a prequel, about the early life of the pig who supplied the ring.

Born in 1812, the twentieth of 21 children, Edward Lear was a sickly child with a weak chest, poor eyesight and epilepsy. He was reared by his oldest sister, Ann, and despite little education developed an early talent for drawing and painting. By the age of eighteen he was earning a modest living doing detailed paintings of birds. By 1837 Lear's poor health forced him abroad, and he travelled around Europe painting landscapes, eventually settling in Italy. Lear had been writing absurd verse since he was a child, and in 1846 he published *A Book of Nonsense*, the first of several books of amusing drawings and rhymes which made him famous. For many years he was remembered more for these than his artistic work, but he is now recognised as one of England's leading bird painters.

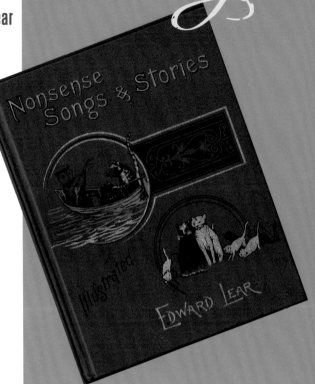

"Pussy said to the Owl, 'You elegant fowl!
How charmingly sweet you sing!
O let us be married! too long we have tarried:
But what shall we do for a ring?'
They sailed away, for a year and a day,
To the land where the Bong-tree grows
And there in a wood a Piggy-wig stood
With a ring at the end of his nose,
His nose,
His nose,
With a ring at the end of his nose.

'Dear pig, are you willing to sell for one shilling
Your ring?' Said the Piggy, 'I will.'
So they took it away, and were married next day
By the Turkey who lives on the hill.
They dined on mince, and slices of quince,
Which they ate with a runcible spoon;
And hand in hand, on the edge of the sand,
They danced by the light of the moon,
The moon,
The moon,
They danced by the light of the moon."

Neil Gaiman

BADGER

"There was the noise of a bolt shot back, and the door opened a few inches, enough to show a long snout and a pair of sleepy blinking eyes. 'Now the *very* next time this happens,' said a gruff and suspicious voice, 'I shall be exceedingly angry. Who is it *this* time, disturbing people on such a night? Speak up!'**"**

It never struck me as one of the best ideas. Neil Gaiman as Badger? Hmm. As a medieval swash-buckling hero maybe, or a dark overlord from another time zone perhaps. Or even the lead singer in a very cool band. But Badger from *Wind in the Willows*! And then an odd thing happened. He just started to become Badger, literally, in front of my eyes. With wonderfully simple make-up and exquisite robes he started to move like Badger, he started to smile like Badger, he even started to talk as I imagine Badger talks. When we finally went on set and gave him his chair and book he just was Badger. (Though truthfully he'd also make a very good stand-in for the punk group The Damned.)

Cambridge Jones

WHO IS NEIL GAIMAN?

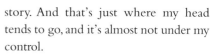

Neil Gaiman grew up in the Sussex countryside, but spent most of his time in libraries, devouring books and comics, memorising *Alice's Adventures in Wonderland* and wishing he had thought of writing *The Lord of the Rings* before J. R. R. Tolkien. He was so certain that he wanted to be a writer that he skipped university and went straight into journalism.

After writing biographies of the pop group Duran Duran and author Douglas Adams, Neil worked on graphic novels and *Sandman*, a 75-issue comic series that gained cult status. Since then he has written in many forms: picture books like *The Wolves in the Walls*; children's stories like *The Graveyard Book*; adult novels like *The Ocean at the End of the Lane*; screenplays like *Neverwhere*; and television episodes for *Doctor Who*. He keeps bees, and has nearly 2 million followers on Twitter.

CAMBRIDGE JONES:
Who is your character, and why did you choose him?

NEIL GAIMAN: My character is Badger from *The Wind in the Willows* by Kenneth Grahame. Growing up, I loved *The Wind in the Willows*. And then I rediscovered it as an adult, reading it to my own children. And discovered that it was just as deep and smart and peculiar a book as it had been when I was a child. If anything it had got better and deeper. As a kid, I think I identified with Mole, coming out into a new world, getting tangled up with Toad, getting tangled up with Rat, going on all these strange adventures. And then I think, probably in my twenties, I identified with Toad. Because I was bumptious and certain the world would take care of me, and willing to go out there and have mad adventures and have my friends pick up the pieces.

And now I am a respectable gentleman, and of a certain age. And really I identify enormously with Badger. Somebody who just likes his chair and will sleep with a handkerchief over his face or read the paper or drowse off. But is willing to pick up a cudgel and head off to wallop weasels and ferrets and stoats if it's necessary. And I like Badger because he's smart. He is irascible, but he has earned his irascibility. And also he has great hair. And, you know, if you're going to be your favourite literary character, I think the first thing you have to do is go, "OK, what hair are we talking about here?" And Badger is gonna win. Every time.

CJ: Why did you become a storyteller?

NG: I don't know that I had any option. It's not like I woke up one day and said, "I'm now going to give up my dreams of becoming an astronaut and I'm gonna become a storyteller instead." I have the kind of mind that makes up stories, that loves playing with myth, that loves taking little elements and trying to figure out how they work and building them into a story. And that's just where my head tends to go, and it's almost not under my control.

As a child my favourite subject was English. My favourite things to do were essays, when essays allowed you to make stuff up. I loved making stuff up. As a kid I had less to make stuff up about, or so I thought. When I was a kid, I read books. And because my experiences were so far away from those of people in books, I thought that I didn't have any stories. If you were in a story, you'd get to defeat smugglers or German spies or bank robbers, or you discovered your geography teacher was an evil fifth columnist and hiding the plans to the missile base next door to the school inside hollowed-out vegetable marrows. And there weren't any missile bases next to my school and I wasn't quite sure what a hollowed-out vegetable marrow would look like, let alone confident in my ability to catch a fifth columnist. But as I grow older I'm much more likely now to look back and go, you know, there really was magic happening, the raw stuff of story was still going on. Now all I need to do is take that out and play with it.

We all have imaginations. You cannot downplay the importance of the imagination. Anything that we can see, that isn't a rock or a tree, is there because someone imagined it. Everything. Chairs. Somebody at some point had to go, "Wouldn't it be a good idea to make a thing you can sit on?" Other people had to go, "That will never catch on! A chair? Are you mad? I'm not sitting on one of those. The ground was good enough for my dad and his dad before him." And somebody invented a chair.

I think storytelling comes from the same impulse. We look around at the world and we go, it doesn't have to be like this. And if it is like this, I could be something different. And what that something different is, we get to find out.

The Wind in the Willows

by Kenneth Grahame

THE STORY

One spring morning, gentle, home-loving Mole ventures out into the sunshine. Ratty invites him to stay and introduces him to the delights of "messing about in boats" and then to his rich and impetuous friend, Toad. Ratty and Mole despair as Toad careers from one craze to another, crashing his boats, horse-drawn caravan and motor car, and wasting a fortune on fines. Ratty is convinced that his friend Badger could control Toad, but Badger lives in the Wild Wood and is rarely seen. Eventually Mole sets off to find the elusive creature, only to get lost and scared and tormented by weasels in the snowy darkness...

The Wind in the Willows grew out of the years that Kenneth Grahame spent with his grandmother at Cookham Dene beside the River Thames. Grahame was born in Edinburgh in 1859, but was sent south at the age of five when his mother died and his grief-stricken father went to live abroad. Grahame excelled at school, but could not afford to go to university so worked as a clerk at the Bank of England and wrote in his spare time.

He published two successful collections of short stories, but it was not until ten years later that he returned to the riverbank in bedtime stories and then letters for his young son Alastair. The Wind in the Willows was rejected by several publishers before it was eventually published in 1908, and initially it received terrible reviews. But it was championed by famous fans such as President Roosevelt and A. A. Milne, author of Winnie-the-Pooh, who adapted it into a play. Word spread, sales grew and it soon became a treasured classic.

First published without pictures, The Wind in the Willows has been illustrated more than 90 times, most famously by Ernest Shepard, who also drew the illustrations for Winnie-the-Pooh.

" 'O, Badger,' cried the Rat, 'let us in, please. It's me, Rat, and my friend Mole, and we've lost our way in the snow.'

'What, Ratty, my dear little man!' exclaimed the Badger, in quite a different voice. 'Come along in, both of you, at once. Why, you must be perished. Well I never! Lost in the snow! And in the Wild Wood too, and at this time of night! But come in with you.'

The two animals tumbled over each other in their eagerness to get inside, and heard the door shut behind them with great joy and relief.

The Badger, who wore a long dressing gown, and whose slippers were indeed very down-at-heel, carried a flat candlestick in his paw and had probably been on his way to bed when their summons sounded. He looked kindly down on them and patted both their heads. 'This is not the sort of night for small animals to be out,' he said paternally. 'I'm afraid you've been up to some of your pranks again, Ratty. But come along; come into the kitchen. There's a first-rate fire there, and supper and everything.' "

From The Wind in the Willows, Chapter IV

WHO IS BADGER?

Badger is a stern but kindly character who lives alone in the middle of the Wild Wood, and at the heart of Kenneth Grahame's much-loved animal story. We have to wait until Chapter IV to meet him properly, but by the time we do, we are as curious as Mole to get to know this "important personage" who "hates Society and invitations, and dinner, and all that sort of thing".

Jamila Gavin
HANUMAN THE MONKEY GOD

> "Hanuman bowed before Sugriva, the king of the monkeys, and said, 'Sugriva, I have magic powers. If it is the demons who have kidnapped Sita, then she could be on the island of Lanka, in the palace of King Ravana. Why don't you let me fly to the island and see if I can find her?'"

Have you ever had a car journey that you never wanted to end? A conversation that you feel had only just started several hours in? A person you meet who you feel you've known for ever, and want to know for ever and a day? If you haven't, I suggest you try working with Jamila Gavin and then drive her from Oxford to London in heavy traffic. All of the above will become true in a trice. What an honour!

Cambridge Jones

WHO IS JAMILA GAVIN?

Jamila Gavin was born in Mussoorie, India, and spent her early childhood playing amongst the sugar canes in the foothills of the Himalayas. Her Indian father and English mother had met as teachers in Iran, and from them she inherited a strong sense of belonging to two rich cultures. As she grew up, Jamila lived in an Indian palace in Punjab, a flat in a bombed-out street in Shepherd's Bush, London, a bungalow in Poona, and London again, in a terraced house in Ealing, where she was the only Asian child in her school.

Jamila studied music in London, Paris and Berlin before working in the music department of the BBC. When she had children, she decided to write, setting up a desk in her chilly garden shed. Her first collection of short stories, *The Magic Orange Tree*, was published in 1979. Since then she has written over 40 novels and collections, including *Grandpa Chatterji*, *The Surya Trilogy* and the award-winning *Coram Boy*, which was adapted for the stage. Jamila believes that Asian and black children's lives are not sufficiently reflected in books, and wants her stories to help to redress this balance.

Q & A

CAMBRIDGE JONES: So, Jamila, who is your favourite character, and why?

JAMILA GAVIN: I've got lots of favourite characters in literature, because I've always loved reading. But I decided to choose Hanuman because he incorporates everything that I've loved about stories and childhood. I was born in India. The monkey was very early on my favourite animal. I would have had a monkey for a pet if I could. And Hanuman is such a fantastic character and leads me into one of my most favourite Indian stories, which is the story of Rama and Sita in the *Ramayana*. So, he was a natural choice.

I think one of the wonderful things about India and Hinduism is the *fun* that you get with all the festivals and the gods and the stories. Religion really permeates every form of expression, whether it's dance, theatre, music. So when I was hearing stories of Hanuman and the *Ramayana*, there would have been storytellers coming through the villages, maybe round about the time of Diwali, which celebrates the return home of Rama and Sita from their long exile, and Sita's kidnapping by Ravana, the ten-headed demon. They're all images that children adore, I adored.

CJ: Why did you become a storyteller?

JG: I think I was always a natural storyteller, maybe because my mother was a very good storyteller. I was born in a small village on the outskirts of a town in Northern India and there weren't libraries and bookshops, so all my stories came from my mother's storytelling. I can remember going for walks with her. I must have been very young, under six, and she would tell me the story of the book that she had, because she came from England with a great trunk full of books. It might be Agatha Christie or Dostoyevsky, but I would get some kind of version. And I think that entered my blood. I know that on voyages on the ship from India to England I would gather children round and tell stories.

Funnily enough, music was my passion. I would often tell stories from the piano and illustrate with music. Storytelling was just something I did, as one eats and drinks. It was a long time before I focused on making storytelling part of my professional life, because I went into the BBC and did programmes that were about music.

There was a point where I had to think, "How do I find my way into the written word?" And I found that letter-writing was my intermediary art form, if you want to call it an art form. I seemed to be able to write letters with a kind of spontaneity: in fact it was someone reading my letters

saying, "You really ought to be a writer." I've always needed to remember the rhythms of storytelling, and work with that in my writing.

CJ: If I said, for the rest of your life, you can only write stories or tell stories, which would you choose?

JG: I might choose "tell". I think the importance about telling stories is the audience. I don't like reading from a book. I much prefer to have the story in my head and be able to make eye contact with the listener and adapt the story accordingly. I'm sure this is what happens with all the great religious stories – the *Ramayana*, the *Mahabharata*, possibly the same with the *Iliad* and the *Odyssey*. These were told by storytellers who would have been judging their listeners and the circumstances in which they were telling. So they might want to emphasise this rather than that.

In the story of the *Ramayana*, I often find myself emphasising the fact that it was all about promises, and how promises always get compromised or broken. I find it very touching when Hanuman flies across the Ocean to look for Sita and lands on the Island of Lanka. He changes himself into a cat and creeps around the palace, going in and out of all the doors, seeing if he can find her. Ravana was a musician and he tried to woo Sita with music, and she was just steadfast: "No, I am married to Rama, he's my husband." When Hanuman comes he finds her banished to the gardens and her hair is all loose, which is always a sign of mourning and sadness for an Indian woman. He coils his tail around a branch of a tree and hangs down until his mouth is close to her ear. And he says, "Don't be afraid, your husband is coming to rescue you!" and it's a lovely moment.

WHO IS HANUMAN?

Hanuman, the Hindu monkey god, is one of the most popular figures in Indian religion. He appears in the oral epic, the *Ramayana*, which was first written down by the poet Valmiki some time between 500 BC and AD 400, though he may be based on a tribal deity who dates as far back as 6000 BC.

There are many stories of Hanuman's birth and early adventures as a brave and inquisitive young monkey. In one he tries to reach the sun, thinking it is a ripe fruit. Surya, the sun god, is so impressed that he grants Hanuman immortality and goes on to become his teacher.

Hanuman is often pictured holding a mountain in his palm. This relates to a famous episode in the *Ramayana* when Rama's brother Lakshmana is badly wounded and Hanuman is sent to the Himalayas to fetch some magical, life-saving herbs. Hanuman cannot recognise the herbs, so tears up the whole mountain and brings it back to Rama. The herbs are found and Lakshmana is cured.

Hanuman's main story is told in the *Ramayana*, one of two great Indian epics, the other being the *Mahabharata*. The *Ramayana* begins in heaven, with the gods Vishnu and Lakshmi deciding to visit earth as Rama and Sita and rid it of demons. When Sita is kidnapped

by the King of the Demons, Hanuman finds and rescues her, leading Rama's monkey army in the Battle of Lanka and single-handedly killing many demons including their king. The story ends with Rama, Sita and their followers crossing India, their path lit by lamps that people have put on their doorsteps. This is celebrated every autumn as Diwali, the festival of lights.

Hanuman appears in many paintings, poems, songs and stories as an example of devotion and service and an inspiration for people who need to conquer obstacles in their own lives. His birth is celebrated each spring with the Hanuman Jayanti festival.

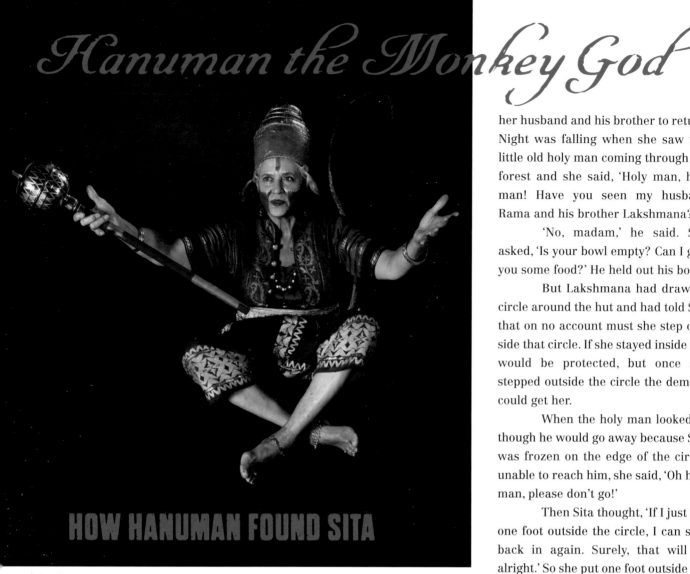

HOW HANUMAN FOUND SITA

"In an Indian forest, two princes are making their way along a trail, looking and looking. Every animal they pass they ask, 'Have you seen Sita? Have you seen Sita?'

Now Sita was a princess and the wife of Prince Rama, and it was Prince Rama and his brother, Lakshmana, who were now moving south through the jungle where the animals roamed and the demons were hiding. And it was demons they thought had kidnapped Rama's wife Sita.

Rama had been exiled from the city of Ayodhya because his stepmother had wanted her son to rule instead of Rama, so Rama had been banished into the jungle for fourteen years.

Lakshmana had accompanied him, but Sita had insisted on staying with her husband, and she too had gone with them. But the king of the demons, Ravana, had spotted Sita and fallen in love with her. He had tricked her into seeing a deer, and then tricked Rama into hunting that deer.

And when Rama went off to hunt the deer, and didn't come back, and when Lakshmana went off to look for Rama, and didn't come back, Sita waited and waited for her husband and his brother to return. Night was falling when she saw this little old holy man coming through the forest and she said, 'Holy man, holy man! Have you seen my husband Rama and his brother Lakshmana?'

'No, madam,' he said. Sita asked, 'Is your bowl empty? Can I give you some food?' He held out his bowl.

But Lakshmana had drawn a circle around the hut and had told Sita that on no account must she step outside that circle. If she stayed inside she would be protected, but once she stepped outside the circle the demons could get her.

When the holy man looked as though he would go away because Sita was frozen on the edge of the circle, unable to reach him, she said, 'Oh holy man, please don't go!'

Then Sita thought, 'If I just put one foot outside the circle, I can step back in again. Surely, that will be alright.' So she put one foot outside the circle and reached to put the food in his bowl.

And 'Whooo!' he turned into the ten-headed demon king, Ravana. He snatched her under his arm, clicked his fingers and from out of the sky came a demon chariot with demon horses. And he flung her in and they galloped away.

Meanwhile Rama and his brother Lakshmana were looking everywhere for Sita. They went on and on moving south when suddenly from out of the trees fell some monkeys, monkey warriors with spears!

'Halt!' they said. 'What are you doing in our territory? Who are you? Where do you come from?'

Rama said, 'I am Prince Rama, from the city of Ayodhya and this is my brother Prince Lakshmana. Take me to your king.'

So the monkey warriors leapt ahead, guarding the two princes, and took them before King Sugriva, the monkey king. Sugriva sat there on his throne and Rama and Lakshmana bowed before him and explained who they were.

'I am Rama and this is my brother, Lakshmana, and we are looking for my wife, the Princess Sita. We fear she has been kidnapped.'

Sugriva had heard of Rama and Lakshmana and the city of Ayodhya and he made them welcome and gave them food and new clothes. After they had rested for a while he summoned all the monkeys.

'Does anybody know anything about this? Has anybody seen Sita?'

Then one monkey said, 'Well, I did see a chariot flying through the sky and from out of the chariot tumbled a bracelet.'

Sugriva said, 'Have you got that bracelet?'

And the monkey said, 'Yes,' and handed it to him. Sugriva said to Rama, 'Is this Sita's bracelet? Do you recognise it?'

Rama's eyes filled with tears. 'It could be,' he said, 'but I'm not sure.'

And then stepped forward Hanuman.

Now, Hanuman was the son of the wind god, Vayu, and he had magic powers. He could make himself as small as the tiniest flea or as big as a mountain. He could make himself invisible. He could fly around the world in 30 seconds. And Hanuman, although he was a god, was the general of King Sugriva's monkey army.

But he stepped forward and bowed before Sugriva and said, 'Sugriva, I have magic powers. If it is the demons who have kidnapped Sita, then she could be on the island of Lanka, in the palace of King Ravana, the king of the demons. Why don't you let me fly over to the island and see if I can find her?'

So Sugriva gave his permission and Hanuman, in a flash, turned himself into an invisible wind and blew himself over the ocean from the southern tip of India to the island of Lanka. When he reached the island, he turned himself into a little cat. And who takes any notice of a cat, creeping into the palace, going up and down the crystal staircases, in and out of chambers looking everywhere for Sita? But she wasn't to be found in the palace, so the little cat crept outside, hopped onto the wall, changed himself back into a monkey and began to swing through the trees of the palace gardens. As he swung further and further, the gardens grew denser, and deeper, and darker.

Then suddenly he heard this grunting, and moaning, and pinching, and scratching, and there Hanuman saw a beautiful maiden, her hair all long and unmade up, weeping under a tree. And he knew this was Sita. Hanuman leapt up onto the tree and coiled his tail around the branch and hung upside down until his mouth was close to Sita's ear.

'Sita,' he whispered. 'Be brave. Your husband is near. Prince Rama is going to come and rescue you.' Sita looked up with absolute joy on her face.

But what Hanuman also saw were the bruises and the pinches and the tearstains on her cheeks, and it made him so angry to think that the demons had treated this beautiful princess in such a cruel way he lost his temper. And in losing his temper, he began to grow bigger, and bigger, and bigger, until he became a giant monkey, ripping trees from their roots and hurling them around. He began to fight and kill as many demons as he could.

More demons came pouring out and flung themselves on top of Hanuman until, even with his size, he was covered in demons, pinning him down to the ground. They dragged him before Ravana. Ravana, with his ten whirling heads. And the demons said, 'We found this monkey talking to the Princess Sita! And he says he's come from Rama! What shall we do with him? Kill! Kill! Kill!'

But Ravana said, 'Killing is too good for him. What is it a monkey treasures more than anything? Why, it is his tail!'

He ordered a fiery brand to be brought and he took the brand and they held out Hanuman's tail and he set it ablaze. Hanuman stood there for a moment with his tail on fire, then he used his magic powers and became smaller, smaller, smaller, smaller, smaller, smaller. And when he was so, so small, he slipped out of their clutches and went leaping all over the demon city. And with his tail he set the city on fire.

Finally he turned himself back into a wind and flew over the ocean. He tried to dip his tail into the water to put out the fire, but it wouldn't go out. In the end he had to put it into his mouth and suck it hard, and at last it was extinguished.

He reached the mainland and went to Rama and Lakshmana and King Sugriva and he said, 'I have found Sita.'

Then they gathered their armies together and went to the shore, and looked across the ocean to the island of Lanka. Rama wept. 'How are we to cross the waves?'

'By building a bridge,' cried Hanuman and the monkeys. They gathered up rocks and boulders, and trees from the forest, and in seven days they built a bridge across to Ravana's island. There was a mighty battle, and thousands died on both sides. Finally, Rama slew Ravana and his ten heads with one golden arrow and the battle was won. But where was Sita? Hanuman went in search of her. He found Sita, and led the princess before her husband and said, 'Prince Rama, receive thy wife.' "

Transcribed from a live storytelling by Jamila Gavin at the Story Museum, 2014

Frances Hardinge
THE SCARLET PIMPERNEL

“ 'The Scarlet Pimpernel, Mademoiselle,'
he said at last, 'is the name of a humble English
wayside flower; but it is also the name chosen
to hide the identity of the best and bravest
man in all the world, so that he may better
succeed in accomplishing the noble task he
has set himself to do.' ”

You may seek him in the portrait we made with Frances Hardinge, but you will seek in vain, I fear, for this is Sir Percy Blakeney you are looking at. Very few people actually get to see the real Scarlet Pimpernel... And so it might seem with the lovely Frances Hardinge, who manages to be open, warm and friendly while retaining a real sense of mystery, as though she too may have a double life. I suspect we will never know...
Cambridge Jones

WHO IS FRANCES HARDINGE?

Frances was born in Brighton in 1973 and grew up in a series of "small, sinister villages", moving at the age of seven to a huge old house on a hilltop in Kent that "wuthered when the wind blew". She always made up stories and especially liked dark tales. Frances studied English at Oxford University, then worked for a software company, writing short stories for adults in her spare time, until a friend, children's author Rhiannon Lassiter, persuaded her to try writing for children. When her story *Fly By Night* was published, it received rave reviews and several prizes, allowing Frances to become a full-time author. Now on her sixth book, Frances is rarely seen without a black hat which, she says, feels like part of her head, and may contain her personality.

Q & A

CAMBRIDGE JONES: So, Frances, who is your character, and why did you choose him?

FRANCES HARDINGE: My character is the Scarlet Pimpernel, for a number of different reasons, the most important being that I've always had a thing for tricksters. Another possibility that I was considering was Puss in Boots, who is again, like the Scarlet Pimpernel, a con artist you're allowed to back. The Scarlet Pimpernel doesn't just think faster than his enemies, he thinks in a completely different way. He takes advantages of their blind spots, their deference to authority, the people they don't pay attention to, and he has industrial quantities of cheek.

I read it when I was quite young, I think about ten or eleven, and very much enjoyed the adventures, particularly the Scarlet Pimpernel's cleverness and courage. Now I would have one or two more questions that I would ask him, such as where was he before the Revolution? Why wasn't he rescuing any of the oppressed masses who were being driven by desperation and penury to the brink of revolution? How come he only got involved when the people with pretty clothes and nice manners were in danger? But even aside from that, he's still very swashbuckling.

CJ: And why did you become a storyteller?

FH: I didn't have any choice. I was always a storyteller. I think I've always had stories I wanted to tell. Even when I was very young I remember telling my sister stories when we were both trying to get to sleep – serial style, a little bit each night. And I was scrawling stories down from the time I could hold a pencil.

THE STORY

It is 1792, and France is gripped by revolution. Every day aristocrats face death by guillotine. But someone is helping these "aristos" to escape. Someone ingenious and daring, a formidable swordsman, a master of disguise. Who with each rescue taunts his enemies by leaving a note signed simply with a drawing of a small red flower, a scarlet pimpernel.

Marguerite St Just is a beautiful French actress, fascinated by this hero, and disappointed by her shallow, dandyish husband, the English nobleman Sir Percy Blakeney. Chauvelin, a French government agent, tricks Marguerite into helping him discover the true identity of the elusive Pimpernel...

Baroness Emma Orczy was born in Hungary in 1865. Fearing a peasant revolution, her family fled the country three years later, eventually settling in London when she was fifteen. Emma went to art school where she met and married the Englishman Montague Barstow. Together they scraped a living translating and illustrating stories.

In her mid-thirties, following a trip to Paris, Orczy imagined the character of Sir Percy as she stood waiting for an underground train. She wrote *The Scarlet Pimpernel* in five weeks. The novel was rejected by a dozen publishers, but was adapted into a stage play which, despite bad reviews, broke box-office records. Published in 1905, its popularity encouraged Orczy to write seventeen more adventures for her "reckless daredevil" and made her and Barstow rich. *The Scarlet Pimpernel* has been widely adapted for television, films and musicals, and has inspired memorable storylines for *Doctor Who*, *Daffy Duck* and *Blackadder*.

The Scarlet Pimpernel

by Baroness Orczy

" The guards at the gates had been doubled, the sergeants in command had been threatened with death, whilst liberal rewards were offered for the capture of these daring and impudent Englishmen. There was a sum of five thousand francs promised to the man who laid hands on the mysterious and elusive Scarlet Pimpernel.

Everyone felt that Bibot would be that man, and Bibot allowed that belief to take firm root in everybody's mind; and so, day after day, people came to watch him at the West Gate, so as to be present when he laid hands on any fugitive aristo who perhaps might be accompanied by that mysterious Englishman.

'Bah!' he said to his trusted corporal, 'Citoyen Grospierre was a fool! Had it been me now, at that North Gate last week …'

Citoyen Bibot spat on the ground to express his contempt for his comrade's stupidity.

'How did it happen, Citoyen?' asked the corporal.

'Grospierre was at the gate, keeping good watch,' began Bibot, pompously, as the crowd closed in round him, listening eagerly to his narrative. 'We've all heard of this meddlesome Englishman, this accursed Scarlet Pimpernel. He won't get through MY gate, morbleu!, unless he be the devil himself. But Grospierre was a fool. The market carts were going through the gates; there was one laden with casks, and driven by an old man, with a boy beside him. Grospierre was a bit drunk, but he thought himself very clever; he looked into the casks – most of them, at least – and saw they were empty, and let the cart go through.'

A murmur of wrath and contempt went round the group of ill-clad wretches, who crowded round Citoyen Bibot.

'Half an hour later,' continued the sergeant, 'up comes a captain of the guard with a squad of some dozen soldiers with him. "Has a cart gone through?" he asks of Grospierre, breathlessly. "Yes," says Grospierre, "not half an hour ago." "And you have let them escape," shouts the captain furiously. "You'll go to the guillotine for this, citoyen sergeant! that cart held concealed the ci-devant Duc de Chalis and all his family!" "What!" thunders Grospierre, aghast. "Aye! and the driver was none other than that cursed Englishman, the Scarlet Pimpernel." '

A howl of execration greeted this tale. Citoyen Grospierre had paid for his blunder on the guillotine, but what a fool! oh! what a fool!

Bibot was laughing so much at his own tale that it was some time before he could continue.

' "After them, my men," shouts the captain,' he said after a while, ' "remember the reward; after them, they cannot have gone far!" And with that he rushes through the gate followed by his dozen soldiers.'

'But it was too late!' shouted the crowd, excitedly.

'They never got them!'

'Curse that Grospierre for his folly!'

'He deserved his fate!'

'Fancy not examining those casks properly!'

But these sallies seemed to amuse Citoyen Bibot exceedingly; he laughed until his sides ached, and the tears streamed down his cheeks.

'Nay, nay!' he said at last, 'those aristos weren't in the cart; the driver was not the Scarlet Pimpernel!'

'What?'

'No! The captain of the guard was that damned Englishman in disguise, and every one of his soldiers aristos!' "

From *The Scarlet Pimpernel*, Chapter 1

WHO IS THE SCARLET PIMPERNEL?

Tall, broad-shouldered and blue-eyed, Sir Percy Blakeney's good looks are marred by an annoying laugh and inane expression. But we gradually realise this is a cunning disguise.

Some say that the Scarlet Pimpernel is the most influential character in twentieth-century fiction, the first hero with a secret identity, a character who pretends to be foolish to conceal brave deeds for which he expects no reward. This device has since been borrowed by Zorro, Batman, Superman and many others. The Pimpernel is also said to have inspired real-life heroism such as Raoul Wallenberg's rescues of tens of thousands of Hungarian Jews from Nazi concentration camps.

Charlie Higson
BOROMIR

"One Ring to rule them all,
One Ring to find them,
One Ring to bring them all
and in the darkness bind them."

Charlie has the largest collection of kids' freebies and knick-knacks that you are ever likely to set eyes on. Everything from McDonald's free characters to vintage toy cars. It's mad. And many of them are beautifully laid out in glass display cabinets. What a good idea then to set up some studio lighting, dress him up as a warrior hero and let him run around with a sword (my grandfather's sword, in fact). It is something of a small miracle that Charlie still has an intact and complete display in his lovely home.

Cambridge Jones

WHO IS CHARLIE HIGSON?

Charlie Higson is an author, actor, comedian, director and writer for television and radio. While growing up, he wrote plays inspired by the comedians Monty Python and resolutely ignored his father's advice to get a proper job as he could never make any money from writing. After leaving university, Charlie formed a band, The Higsons, and worked as a decorator before teaming up with Paul Whitehouse to create many successful radio and television comedies including *Down the Line* and *The Fast Show*. Charlie has written four adult thrillers and eighteen novels for young people, including the hugely popular *Young Bond* series.

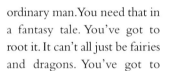

Q & A

CAMBRIDGE JONES: Who is your character, and why did you choose him?

CHARLIE HIGSON: My character is Boromir from *The Lord of the Rings*. And I chose him because I read *Lord of the Rings* when I was fourteen, and it was the first book I remember reading that completely consumed me and took me out of my life and into this whole other imagined world.

I always loved stories like King Arthur and Robin Hood and the Greek myths and legends. Basically if the hero in the story had a sword, I was happy. I just remember not wanting *Lord of the Rings* to ever end, and wanting to spend my whole life in that world.

I had a toss-up: should I go for Boromir or Aragorn? And I thought, I can't quite pull off Aragorn, he's a bit too special for me. The interesting thing about Boromir is he's the main character in the book, who is simply a human. He's not an elf or a dwarf or a whatever Aragorn is, hundreds of years old. He's just an ordinary man.

The first section of *The Lord of the Rings* ends with Boromir trying to steal the ring off Frodo because he thinks it will save his people. And it's a very human thing to do. In the end he can't be as noble even as a hobbit. And as soon as he tries to do it, he realises he's made a terrible mistake, and he sacrifices himself to save Frodo. So it's a really important bit. For me it was when the book really took off.

He wasn't the central character. I mean, it's a sort of Magnificent Seven set-up, with the Fellowship of the Ring. Legolas is a little bit distant, being an elf. Gimli is kind of there for comic value. And the hobbits are hobbits. Boromir, out of all of them, is the only one that's just an

ordinary man. You need that in a fantasy tale. You've got to root it. It can't all just be fairies and dragons. You've got to have characters that you can relate to.

CJ: Why did you become a storyteller?

CH: I became a storyteller because I hooked on to the magic of storytelling when I was a kid. I started writing books aged ten, and I found there was this sort of magic where you could sit down with a blank piece of paper and a biro and, just by writing something down, you could create characters that had never existed before, and tell a story that had never been told before. That power of creativity I just thought was amazing; to be able to make up whole worlds.

I loved the idea of telling stories as well. It's in our genes that we try to see the world in terms of stories. And we see our lives in terms of stories. Everything that happens we try and fit into a story scene. I don't know why that is. Sometimes it's a good thing, sometimes it's a bad thing because you try and make things into a story that aren't stories. But it seems to be innate and very deep-seated in the human psyche. Maybe it's a by-product of us being the only species that uses language, and once you start using language…

I do lots of talks for children. I talk without notes, and I find that if I tell it like a story with a beginning, middle and end, and one thing leading to another, it's a very good way of remembering what I'm saying. So it's a way of remembering things. There's all those memory tricks you can do, aren't there, for how to remember a pack of cards? You imagine going on a walk past familiar objects, and you have the different cards nestled there. I think the idea of stringing things together like that is part of what makes us human.

The Lord of the Rings

by J. R. R. Tolkien

THE STORY

Frodo, a hobbit, has inherited a ring from his uncle Bilbo. The wizard Gandalf suspects this is the sinister "One Ring", and advises Frodo to take it away from his home and the Shire. Frodo leaves with his friend Sam and his cousins, Merry and Pippin. After escaping the terrifying Ringwraiths, they meet Aragorn, who guides them to Rivendell. It is decided that Frodo must return the Ring to the flames of Mount Doom in Mordor, where it was forged. The Fellowship of the Ring is formed to protect him: the hobbits, Aragorn, Gandalf, Gimli the dwarf, Legolas the Elf and Boromir, a man. They set forth on a long and perilous quest...

The Lord of the Rings is an epic fantasy by Oxford University professor John Ronald Reuel Tolkien. Written between 1937 and 1949 to follow Tolkien's *The Hobbit*, it has sold over 150 million copies and inspired dramatisations, parodies, computer games, music and a large body of fantasy literature, as well as record-breaking films. The trilogy draws on Tolkien's love of fairy tales, research on mythology and languages, and experiences in the First World War. Described as one of the greatest works of imaginative fiction of the twentieth century, it has been voted the nation's favourite book in Britain, Germany and Australia.

Tolkien was born in Africa in 1892. His father died when he was three, so his mother and younger brother settled near her parents in Birmingham. When he was twelve, his mother also died, and the boys were placed in the care of a Catholic priest. At sixteen Tolkien fell in love with fellow lodger Edith Bratt, but was forbidden to have any contact with her until he came of age. He wrote to Edith immediately after his 21st birthday, declaring his feelings and proposing marriage. They were soon wed, and went on to have four children. Their son Christopher continues to edit his father's work.

TOLKIEN
The Fellowship of the Ring
REVISED EDITION

WHO IS BOROMIR?

Boromir is the brother of Faramir and favourite elder son of the last Steward of Gondor. He carries the Horn of Gondor, a great horn that can summon Gondor's aid if heard within its borders. "A tall man with a fair and noble face, dark-haired and grey-eyed, proud and stern of glance," Boromir is a skilful commander who has battled bravely against the evil forces of Mordor.

❝ 'Come, come, my friend!' said Boromir in a softer voice. 'Why not get rid of it? Why not be free of all your doubt and fear? You can lay the blame on me, if you will. You can say I was too strong and took it by force. For I am too strong for you, halfling,' he cried; and suddenly he sprang over the stone and leaped at Frodo. His fair and pleasant face was hideously changed; a raging fire was in his eyes.

Frodo dodged aside and again put the stone between them. There was only one thing he could do – trembling he pulled out the Ring upon its chain and quickly slipped it on his finger, even as Boromir sprang at him again. The Man gasped, stared for a moment amazed, and then ran wildly about, seeking here and there among the rocks and trees.

'Miserable trickster!' he shouted. 'Let me get my hands on you! Now I see your mind. You will take the ring to Sauron and sell us all. You have only waited your chance to leave us in the lurch. Curse you and all halflings to death and darkness!' Then, catching his foot upon a stone, he fell sprawling and lay upon his face. For a while he was still as if his own curse had struck him down; then suddenly he wept.

He rose and passed a hand over his eyes, dashing away the tears. 'What have I said?' he cried. 'What have I done? Frodo, Frodo!' he called. 'Come back! A madness took me, but it has passed. Come back!' ❞

From *The Fellowship of the Ring* (Book One of *The Lord of the Rings* trilogy), Chapter X

Anthony Horowitz
DR JEKYLL & MR HYDE

"What he told me in the next hour I cannot bring my mind to set on paper. I saw what I saw, I heard what I heard, and my soul sickened at it; and yet, now that the sight has faded from my eyes I ask myself if I believe it, and I cannot answer..."

There are people who instinctively value and appreciate photography and there are those who regard it as a necessary evil. I would hazard a guess that Anthony is in the latter camp. If this is true, then we compounded the ordeal he was about to put himself through by providing a costume that was the wrong size. Somehow, with creative zeal and no small effort on Anthony's part, we managed nevertheless to produce one of my favourite shoots in the series. As I drove Anthony to the station afterwards he seemed a touch bemused that someone could earn a living from photography. But all that melted into insignificance once we realised we were both learning Greek and had a profound love of all things Hellenic!

Cambridge Jones

WHO IS ANTHONY HOROWITZ?

Anthony Horowitz is a prolific writer and screen writer with a special talent for mystery and suspense. Born in Middlesex into a wealthy family, he had an unhappy childhood and a miserable time at his first boarding school. He grew up loving stories, from Tintin to James Bond, and asked for a typewriter on his eighth birthday. Horowitz studied English at the University of York and published his first book at 22. Since then he has written over 60 books, four films and numerous television dramas, creating and writing such popular series as *Foyle's War*, *Collision* and *Injustice*. He was commissioned to write a Sherlock Holmes sequel and his well-known Alex Rider stories have sold over 19 million copies and been made into a film.

Q & A

CAMBRIDGE JONES: Who is your character, and why did you choose him?

ANTHONY HOROWITZ: Well, actually I'm two characters: Dr Jekyll and Mr Hyde. The reason I chose them is that I've always loved the book, and I've always loved Robert Louis Stevenson for that matter. But in Jekyll and Hyde he created this extraordinary truth about humanity, which is that we are, on the face of it, civilised and respectable and good and proper, but inside us lurks the Beast. And Mr Hyde is not a monster; he's not exactly a killer sort of psychopath. He's just that sort of lingering evil and wildness in all of us. And I think that's fascinating. And it's really exciting to be bringing that out of myself.

CJ: And why did you become a storyteller?

AH: I became a storyteller at a very early age. Because I was sent to a particularly horrible boarding school in North London where I was very unhappy; where teachers constantly told me I was a waste of space and useless and would amount to nothing. And it was a very brutal environment and the teachers were abusive in almost every sense of that word. And at night, in the dormitories where we slept, the other children and I were always very scared. And out of nowhere, I started telling stories. They were escape stories about two boys escaping from a school and having adventures around the world. And in telling these stories, first of all, it was a sort of escape from day-to-day life in the school, but also I was rather good at it. And the other children listened to me, and I loved telling these stories. And the next step was to get myself a book and a pen and to start writing stories. And really, by the age of nine or ten, without even knowing it, I was a writer.

Strange Case of Dr Jekyll and Mr Hyde

by Robert Louis Stevenson

THE STORY

John Utterson, a lawyer, becomes concerned that his friend Dr Henry Jekyll is being blackmailed by a sinister figure named Edward Hyde. He eventually confronts Jekyll, who reassures him and asks to be left alone. A year passes. Then one night Hyde is seen beating an elderly man to death, and the murder weapon is found in Jekyll's home. Jekyll explains that Hyde has gone, and produces Hyde's farewell note as evidence. That evening Utterson's clerk points out that Hyde's handwriting and Jekyll's look remarkably similar...

✳ ✳ ✳

Strange Case of Dr Jekyll and Mr Hyde (it acquired a '*The*' later) was published in 1886 and is the fifth novel by Robert Louis Stevenson, exploring his fascination with the good and evil in people's personalities. Born in Edinburgh in 1850, Stevenson was a sickly child, often confined indoors with his books and toy theatre while other children played outside. Although keen to become a writer, he was urged by his father to study law. He qualified, despite spending most of his time drinking in bars and starting a student society whose motto was "Disregard everything our parents taught us."

Stevenson spent much of his life abroad, searching for a climate that suited his weak chest. In 1889 he bought a large estate on Upolu, a small island in Samoa in the South Pacific. He died there four years later, aged 43, and is still fondly remembered by the locals as "Tusitala", which means "storyteller", and is also a kind of jumping spider.

DR. JEKYLL and MR. HYDE

THE TRANSFORMATION
'GREAT GOD! CAN IT BE?'

WHO ARE DR JEKYLL AND MR HYDE?

Dr Jekyll is "a large, well-made, smooth-faced man of fifty", who is able and kindly and has many friends. He worries that he has an evil side of his nature, and develops a potion which allows him to express it when he wishes by transforming into Edward Hyde, a man with no conscience. Hyde is smaller than Jekyll, but younger and stronger, and is seen being violent and cruel. Witnesses find him detestable, but strangely hard to describe. Gradually Jekyll discovers that he is turning into Hyde.

"... late one accursed night, I compounded the elements, watched them boil and smoke together in the glass, and when the ebullition had subsided, with a strong glow of courage, drank off the potion.

The most racking pangs succeeded: a grinding in the bones, deadly nausea, and a horror of the spirit that cannot be exceeded at the hour of birth or death. Then these agonies began swiftly to subside, and I came to myself as if out of a great sickness. There was something strange in my sensations, something indescribably new and, from its very novelty, incredibly sweet. I felt younger, lighter, happier in body; within I was conscious of a heady recklessness, a current of disordered sensual images running like a mill race in my fancy, a solution of the bonds of obligation, an unknown but not an innocent freedom of the soul. I knew myself, at the first breath of this new life, to be more wicked, tenfold more wicked, sold a slave to my original evil; and the thought, in that moment, braced and delighted me like wine. I stretched out my hands, exulting in the freshness of these sensations; and in the act, I was suddenly aware that I had lost in stature.

There was no mirror, at that date, in my room; that which stands beside me as I write was brought there later on, and for the very purpose of those transformations. ... I crossed the yard, wherein the constellations looked down upon me, I could have thought, with wonder, the first creature of that sort that their unsleeping vigilance had yet disclosed to them; I stole through the corridors, a stranger in my own house; and coming to my room, I saw for the first time the appearance of Edward Hyde."

From *Strange Case of Dr Jekyll and Mr Hyde*, Chapter 1, "Henry Jekyll's full statement of the case"

Katrice Horsley
MARY POPPINS

"As they watched, Jane and Michael saw a curious thing happen. As soon as the shape was inside the gate the wind seemed to catch her up into the air and fling her at the house. It was as though it had flung her first at the gate, waited for her to open it, and then had lifted and thrown her, bag and all, at the front door. The watching children heard a terrific bang, and as she landed the whole house shook. 'How funny! I've never seen that happen before,' said Michael."

Katrice seems to me the keeper of many "looks". She arrives as the travelling storyteller, she metamorphoses into Mary Poppins and then, in another quick shoot afterwards whilst interviewing her, she transforms yet again. The story of her own life and experience is as moving as any of the stories she tells. Some people seem to have been put here on earth to share and give joy. She is one of them, I suspect.

Cambridge Jones

WHO IS KATRICE HORSLEY?

Katrice Horsley was born in Birmingham into a large extended family. She had a speech impairment and did not speak at school until she was thirteen. Instead she immersed herself in reading and writing. Later, working in child play and development, she discovered a flair for telling stories which deepened during six years in Ghana, where storytelling is a part of everyday life. The UK's National Storytelling Laureate (2012–2014), Katrice works as a trainer, adviser and motivational speaker, championing the importance of storytelling in everyone's lives.

Q&A

CAMBRIDGE JONES: So who is your character, and why did you choose her?

KATRICE HORSLEY: My character of choice is Mary Poppins. And one of the reasons that I chose her is because some people refer to me as the modern-day Mary Poppins. I do a huge amount of work with children and I hope that I create some kind of magic for them, in the same way Mary Poppins created magic for the children that she looked after. My Mary Poppins is the book-based Mary Poppins, not from the movie. She is quite different to the character within the movie. A little bit darker. A little bit more sinister. And quite often leaves the children to their own devices. And I think that is what every person who works with children should be doing – allowing children the freedom to create, to discover, to manifest in themselves all of that wonder and that beauty and that engagement.

I read a lot of P. L. Travers's writings as I got a little bit older. A lot of her work is about connection: connection with people, connection with the earth, connection on many different levels. And I think if you're a writer, if you're a human being, I believe you are here to connect in some way. Because if you live your life in isolation, then there's no point living it.

CJ: And why did you become a storyteller?

KH: It's very ironic that I became a storyteller. And it's certainly very ironic that I became the National Laureate, because as a child I didn't speak. I had a very serious speech impediment. But I was stuffed full of stories as a child, even though I myself had difficulty communicating. My parents both told me stories, and my aunts and my uncles: I come from a very large extended family.

So I always had that internal landscape. And as I got older it proved to be an incredibly valuable resource, because my childhood became more difficult. There were times when I felt very alone, very isolated, very confused. And I can clearly remember closing my eyes and disappearing into the world of fantasy, into becoming Rapunzel, into becoming Cinderella, into becoming a character who had control over her own life and destiny. That control was given to me through stories, because I didn't have that in my outside life.

Between fourteen and seventeen, there was a lot of stuff that happened in my family. My mum suffered from depression and sometimes wouldn't be able to be as wonderful as she actually was. I would take out seven library books a week, and I would disappear into those books. I would write poems, I would write stories, I would keep journals and, to me, words were my salvation.

Some young people and some adults go and dance away their pain. Some listen to music. Some take photographs. Some kick around a football. For me, I processed all of that through words, through stories and through reading. And I believe that I am living testament to the power of the spoken word, because I one hundred per cent believe that I would not be here as a successful human being if it hadn't been for stories in my childhood.

It's not so much that they were a rock: I think the stories were a sieve. And I would sift through what mattered and what didn't matter, and I was left with the golden nuggets of importance. The stories help me sift through, work out, practise, play through situations and scenarios.

My background is in child play and child development, and I used to work a lot with stories and found out I had a bit of a knack for it. I know now that one of the main predictors of a child's social, cognitive and emotional success is their vocabulary between birth and eight. You can almost predict a child's GCSE results based on how many words they know at five. So it's not the school they go to, it's not whether their dad's a neuroscientist or a bricklayer, it's not whether they've got computers at home: the most important thing you can do to help your child succeed is communicate, talk with them. And unfortunately what's happening in our society is that that is not taking place – irrespective of social or economic background. And lots of children are starting school not being able to speak.

Mary Poppins
by P. L. Travers

THE STORY

With a gust of wind and an almighty crash, Mary Poppins blows into the lives of the Banks children – Jane, Michael and the twins – and everything changes. She slides up banisters, pulls surprises out of her empty carpet bag and takes the children on a series of extraordinary adventures. They soon learn not to ask how long their favourite nanny will stay...

✳   ✳   ✳

Mary Poppins is the first of eight books about a magical nanny, written by P. L. Travers. Born Helen Lyndon Goff in 1899, Travers grew up in Australia and worked briefly as an actress and dancer, choosing Pamela Linda Travers as her stage name. In 1924, she moved to London, where she earned a living writing poetry and articles and studied psychology, myths and spirituality. In 1934, Travers published *Mary Poppins*, with illustrations by Mary Shepard, daughter of Ernest Shepard, the illustrator of *Winnie-the-Pooh*. The book was an instant hit and, after years of persuasion, Travers reluctantly agreed to let Walt Disney make it into a film. She detested Disney's changes to the story and, despite the film's enormous commercial success, refused permission for a sequel. Travers never married, but adopted a son and spent the rest of her long life in Britain and the USA, writing and studying myths and beliefs.

> 66 'What a funny bag!' he said, pinching it with his fingers.
>
> 'Carpet,' said Mary Poppins, putting her key in the lock.
>
> 'To carry carpets in, you mean?'
>
> 'No. Made of.'
>
> 'Oh,' said Michael. 'I see.' But he didn't – quite.
>
> By this time the bag was open, and Jane and Michael were more than surprised to find it was completely empty.
>
> 'Why,' said Jane, 'there's nothing in it!'
>
> 'What do you mean – nothing?' demanded Mary Poppins, drawing herself up and looking as though she had been insulted. 'Nothing in it, did you say?'
>
> And with that she took out from the empty bag a starched white apron and tied it round her waist. Next she unpacked a large cake of Sunlight Soap, a toothbrush, a packet of hairpins, a bottle of scent, a small folding armchair and a box of throat lozenges.
>
> Jane and Michael stared.
>
> 'But I saw,' whispered Michael. 'I'm sure it was empty.' "

From *Mary Poppins*, Chapter 1, "East Wind"

WHO IS MARY POPPINS?

Mary Poppins is brisk and determined, with a mysterious authority over animals, objects and small children. She never acknowledges her magical powers and appears offended whenever Jane and Michael mention their extraordinary adventures or ask difficult questions. "One more word from that direction," she threatens, "and I'll call the Policeman." Despite her cold and prickly manner, she has many devoted friends and quickly wins the hearts of the Banks children, as well as generations of young readers.

Shirley Hughes LADY BRACKNELL

Clara Vulliamy MISS PRISM

"*Lady Bracknell*: Pray allow me to detain you for a moment. This matter may prove to be one of vital importance to Lord Bracknell and myself. Is this Miss Prism a female of repellent aspect, remotely connected with education?

Chasuble: She is the most cultivated of ladies, and the very picture of respectability.

Lady Bracknell: It is obviously the same person."

As you enter Shirley's home you are immediately greeted by the overwhelming sense of happy family life. It must have been a wonderful home to grow up in. Shirley clearly has a talent for life (as well as storytelling). Clara, her daughter, made a wonderful Miss Prism to accompany Shirley's Lady Bracknell, and we had such fun with the characters and the shoots. As Shirley was bringing her daughter, I decided to take mine along: 11-year-old Sasha Lola, who has always been a great fan of Shirley's work. She was rewarded with an introduction to the original Dogger, who is now kept carefully in a special box.
Cambridge Jones

WHO IS SHIRLEY HUGHES?

Shirley Hughes was born in West Kirby, near Liverpool. She studied fashion design at the Liverpool School of Art and art at the Ruskin School of Drawing and Fine Art in Oxford, where she was encouraged to work in the picture book format. She then moved to Notting Hill, London, and embarked on a freelance career, illustrating books by Noel Streatfeild, Alison Uttley, Ian Seraillier, Dorothy Edwards and many others. When her children were young, Shirley began to write and draw her own picture books, starting with *Lucy and Tom's Day*, which was published in 1960. She has illustrated more than 200 books for other people and written over 70 of her own stories, including the *Alfie* series, the *Olly & Me* series and the much-loved *Dogger*, which was voted the favourite illustrated book ever to win the Greenaway Award.

WHO IS CLARA VULLIAMY?

Clara Vulliamy is the daughter of Shirley Hughes and her architect husband, John Vulliamy. Clara went to university to study history, but after three days realised her mistake and moved to art school, studying at the Chelsea School of Art, the Ruskin School in Oxford and the Royal Academy in London. After illustrating for magazines and newspapers, she started creating her own picture books when her children were small. Her book series include *Martha and the Bunny Brothers*, *Lucky Wish Mouse*, *Muffin*, and *Dixie O'Day*, a car-driving dog, created jointly with her mother. Clara lives in Twickenham with her husband and two grown-up children and shares her attic studio with three guinea pigs.

Q & A

CAMBRIDGE JONES: What characters have you chosen, and why?

SHIRLEY HUGHES: We chose a play, but of course it is a story – dramatised – and we wanted to be a duo, a female duo. I have chosen Lady Bracknell from Oscar Wilde's *The Importance of Being Earnest*, partly because I love all the costume of that era. You put it on and you feel enormously imperious. I think it's a brilliantly funny play. And I just wanted to be Lady Bracknell. There's a Lady Bracknell in me that wants to come out, really! Don't you think, Clara?

CLARA VULLIAMY: I've chosen to be Miss Prism. Mum is the powerful, domineering Lady Bracknell and I am the nervous, anxious governess. And the whole story revolves around a mistake that she has made with a baby and a handbag and a railway station. And the moment we have chosen is when they confront each other about this calamitous error that has taken place.

SH: I think this is one of the most perfect scenes in drama.

CV: When I was young we actually acted *The Importance of Being Earnest* in our family. We had lots of copies and we sat

around and we acted the whole play. There was always a lot of competition to be Lady Bracknell and often it was my dad!

CJ: What made you decide to become storytellers?

SH: I am an illustrator. I draw for a living. I illustrated other people's books long before I did any of my own and I don't regard myself as a writer so much as an illustrator. Writing a picture book text is just very, very sparse writing, something bouncing off visual stuff. And that's really how I started. I had an idea for a book of my own. It was called *Dogger*. It was about a poor old toy that got lost and so I went on and became a writer, but only by accident really. It just happened because I was a visual storyteller. Doing picture books, it's like doing a film, it's *visual* storytelling.

CJ: When you are doing visuals for other people, are you still storytelling?

SH: Doing illustrations for another author is much closer to acting. The author is the main person. They're telling the story and your job is to interpret it, to give it a visual form. If it's a book it's like a little theatre anyway.

CV: Mum and I are working on a book together for the first time – or a series of books – and mum is the author and I am the illustrator. And it is a very exciting project and it's also an honour to be mum's first ever *other illustrator*.

CJ: Clara, how did you become a storyteller?

CV: I've always been a storyteller. I began as a storyteller through pictures. I think I was telling stories with pictures before I could read, and probably before I could even speak properly. There's nothing else I ever wanted to do, which is just as well as there's nothing else I really *can* do. Mum never taught me to write or illustrate, but I suppose I just absorbed it as it was in the very air I breathed.

SH: Well, you did do a lot of life drawing. I think that's basic to a good illustrator. You've got to imagine what people do through movement, and if you don't study what people look like you don't get it right, even if they're *animals*!

CV: Coincidentally we were both art students in Oxford.

SH: Yeah. I was at the Ruskin. At Liverpool first, Liverpool Arts School. Then I thought, I'll get out of the Wirral, where we lived, and I'll go to Oxford and have a *thrilling* time, which I did!

CV: Didn't you go there because you were told there was an ice-rink, when in fact there wasn't?

SH: I was told there was an ice-skating rink there.

CJ: They've built one now.

SH: Have they? There wasn't one then.

CV: It should be the Shirley Hughes ice-rink.

SH: It was a bit of a let-down. But other things were there, on offer, including a very strong academic base. I didn't do illustration. There wasn't an illustration course. And the same happened to you, didn't it? But you did go on to the Royal Academy, but as a painter. Neither of us did illustration as a course.

The Importance of Being Earnest
by Oscar Wilde

THE STORY

Jack Worthing is a young country gentleman who pretends to be Ernest Worthing, an invented brother, when he is in London courting a young lady called Gwendolen. One afternoon he is visiting his friend Algernon when Gwendolen arrives with her formidable mother, Lady Bracknell, giving him a chance to propose. Lady Bracknell interviews Jack (or "Ernest") and is appalled to learn that he was adopted as a baby after being found in a handbag at Victoria Station. She forbids further contact.

Algernon, on discovering that Jack has a pretty young ward called Cecily, decides to visit her in the country and pretends to be the mysterious Ernest. Once her governess, Miss Prism, is out of the way, Cecily is quickly charmed and accepts his proposal. Gwendolen arrives and it initially appears that she and Cecily are engaged to the same Ernest. They are joined by Lady Bracknell, who recognises Miss Prism as the family nursemaid who, 28 years earlier, took her baby son out in the perambulator and never returned...

The Importance of Being Earnest, A Trivial Comedy for Serious People, is the comic masterpiece of Oscar Wilde. Born in Dublin in 1854, Wilde was the second child of William Wilde, a surgeon and folktale collector, and writer Jane Elgee, who hosted a literary salon frequented by poets and storytellers. Wilde studied at Trinity College, Dublin, and then at Oxford University, where he gained a double first in classics. He moved to London in 1879, where he worked as a journalist, reviewer and magazine editor, and wrote poetry and children's stories including *The Happy Prince and Other Tales*. With his elaborate clothes, sparkling wit and glamorous friends, Wilde soon became the darling of fashionable society.

In 1890 Wilde published his first and only novel, *The Picture of Dorian Gray*, before turning to playwriting with a series of society comedies that made him famous. His last play, *The Importance of Being Earnest*, first performed on Valentine's Day 1895, was largely rapturously received, but closed after 86 days when Wilde's homosexual relationships led him to court and then to prison for two years. This destroyed both his health and his fortunes: his wife and sons were forced into bankruptcy and Wilde died in poverty in Paris in 1900. The following year, George Alexander, who had acted the part of Jack Worthing in the original production, revived *The Importance of Being Earnest* in a small theatre in Notting Hill, and it has been widely enjoyed and admired ever since for its cleverness, humour and dazzling wordplay.

" LADY BRACKNELL: Twenty-eight years ago, Prism, you left Lord Bracknell's house, Number 104, Upper Grosvenor Square, in charge of a perambulator that contained a baby of the male sex. You never returned. A few weeks later, through the elaborate investigations of the Metropolitan Police, the perambulator was discovered at midnight standing by itself in a remote corner of Bayswater. It contained the manuscript of a three-volume novel of more than usually revolting sentimentality. *[Miss Prism starts in involuntary indignation.]* But the baby was not there. *[Everyone looks at Miss Prism.]* Prism! Where is that baby? *[A pause.]*

MISS PRISM: Lady Bracknell, I admit with shame that I do not know. I only wish I did. The plain facts of the case are these. On the morning of the day you mention, a day that is forever branded on my memory, I prepared as usual to take the baby out in its perambulator. I had also with me a somewhat old, but capacious hand-bag in which I had intended to place the manuscript of a work of fiction that I had written during my few unoccupied hours. In a moment of mental abstraction, for which I can never forgive myself, I deposited the manuscript in the bassinette and placed the baby in the hand-bag. "

From *The Importance of Being Earnest*, Act III

Below: Oscar Wilde

WHO IS LADY BRACKNELL?

Lady Augusta Bracknell is Algernon's snobbish and domineering aunt, who married well and is determined that her daughter, Gwendolen Fairfax, should do the same. The embodiment of upper-class respectability, Lady Bracknell is inclined to extreme pronouncements on money and marriage, education and virtue, with which Wilde mocked the earnestness of Victorian society and customs, and created many of the play's funniest and most memorable lines. The imposing dowager was famously acted in the 1940s and 1950s by Dame Edith Evans, and more recently by Dame Judi Dench and Dame Maggie Smith.

WHO IS MISS PRISM?

Laetitia Prism is Cecily Cardew's prim governess who lives quietly on Jack's country estate and has romantic feelings for Dr Chasuble, the local rector. She has comparatively few lines in the play, but we soon discover that she occupies a central role in a farce built around a moment of absent-minded confusion between a sentimental novel and a small baby.

Terry Jones
RUPERT THE BEAR

"Says Rupert, 'Mother, may I go,

And take my sledge out in the snow?'

'Why, yes,' she says, so off he flies,

And Algy with a snow man spies...

They do not see, as home they go,

That snow man following them through the snow.

With icy fingers gripping tight,

He shouts, 'Why were you so impolite?'

Straight through the wood he drives the pair;

King Frost's stern messenger is there."

Terry has a house near where I grew up in Wales, in fact near the pub we used to ride to for Sunday lunch, above an old slate mine. But he also lives in a secret location in London town which is both central and in the countryside simultaneously. I'd been there before, but had forgotten how perfect it would be for Rupert Bear – a character that Terry loves deeply and always has. We started with a studio set-up, and it quickly became clear that Terry had somehow absorbed the movement of Rupert Bear perfectly. He could move and take up stances exactly as Rupert does in all those annuals of yesteryear. So we quickly abandoned the studio and went out into the London countryside to capture Rupert behind trees, bouncing through the grass and generally just Ruperting about. I even managed to get away without buying him the pint I owe him. Magic!

Cambridge Jones

WHO IS TERRY JONES?

Terry Jones was born in Colwyn Bay, North Wales, and grew up in Surrey. While at Oxford University he met Michael Palin through student drama. Both went on to work in television, writing and appearing in comedy sketches with other members of the future Monty Python team. Terry was keen to create a new comedy format and helped to develop the "stream of consciousness" style for which – along with its surreal situations, subversive plots, nonsense and wordplay – *Monty Python's Flying Circus* became world famous.

Terry co-directed *Monty Python and the Holy Grail* and directed *Life of Brian* and *The Meaning of Life*. He also adapted and directed *The Wind in the Willows*, appearing as Toad. He continues to write and direct films, television programmes and historical documentaries, and writes poetry and short stories. His books for children include *Fairy Tales*, *Fantastic Stories* and *The Saga of Erik the Viking*, which he also made into a film. He is a former President of the Rupert Bear Society.

Q & A

CAMBRIDGE JONES: Who is your character, and why did you choose him?
TERRY JONES: Well, my character is Rupert Bear, and I chose Rupert Bear because he dominated my early life. I became fascinated by Rupert because of his adventures. I have to say, it's only Alfred Bestall's Rupert Bear that I'm keen on. I didn't like Mary Tourtel's: I thought that was a bit of a wet character. But I think Bestall was a genius. It took me a long time to realise that this was drawn by Bestall because he didn't sign any of the pictures while Mary Tourtel was still alive, and he only started signing them once she died. So I just saw this "Bestall" in the corner of one of the frames, and I thought "Who is that?"

And the reason I chose Rupert Bear is because he lives in this wonderful world of Nutwood, in a little cottage, and yet he goes on the most extraordinary and surreal adventures: a giant flicking him through the sky on a chair, a sea-serpent coming up the river, flying off with all the snowmen through the night sky to King Frost's palace. It's a wonderful world. And I was dragged into it by the 1936 annual. It's just wonderful the way that Alfred Bestall's mind works.

For me it was just totally obvious that I would choose Rupert Bear, because that's the only book I read, actually, until I was about eleven. And then I read Ray Bradbury's *The Illustrated Man*.

CJ: Why did you become a storyteller yourself?

TJ: The reason I became a storyteller was because, when my daughter Sally was five years old, I thought, "Oh! I could read her some fairy tales now. I've always wanted to read her fairy tales. And she's just about old enough to be able to cope with them." And so I bought a copy of the Brothers Grimm and I started reading. I read her Snow White. And in the Brothers Grimm version, the wicked stepmother is punished by being made to put on red-hot iron slippers and dance until she falls down dead. And I thought, "I can't read this to my little five-year-old daughter, I don't want her to go to bed thinking, 'Oh I'm so happy they tortured that old woman to death.'" So the next day I started writing my own stories, fairy tales. And I wrote two the next day and then I tested them on Sally when she got home from nursery. And then the next day I wrote another two stories. The first week I wrote two stories a day. I adjusted them when I read them out to Sally, because I could tell when she was interested and when she wasn't. And then the strike rate went down a bit. The second week, I think it was one a day and then it was two or three days for a single story after that. So I had a collection of 36 fairy tales. And I wanted to publish them, but it took three years to get them published. The intention was writing them for Sally. And then when I realised I had 36 stories, I thought, "Well, that's a bookful there."

Rupert and King Frost

THE STORY

Most Rupert stories begin with Rupert Bear living the cosy, predictable life of a small boy in an idyllic English village between the wars. But then something turns up – a mysterious parcel, a magical kite, a strange invention – that catapults Rupert and his friends into a fantastical adventure in a faraway land...

Rupert Bear is the longest-running children's comic in the world, even continuing through Second World War paper shortages, as it was felt that stopping it would damage national morale. Created by Mary Tourtel, Rupert started in 1920 as a children's cartoon in the *Daily Express* newspaper. He and his friends, Bill Badger, Algy Pug and Pong Ping, were an immediate success. When Tourtel retired in 1935, *Punch* illustrator Alfred Bestall took over, creating 270 adventures during the next 35 years. Currently illustrated by Stuart Trotter, the *Rupert* annuals have appeared every year since 1936 and are said to have sold nearly 100 million copies. The stories have been adapted for television, films and video games, and in 1984 inspired Beatle Paul McCartney to make a short animation, *Rupert and the Frog Song*.

Rupert and King Frost

RUPERT SEES THE PALACE

Upon a snowfield wide they land
Before an icy palace grand;

The snow man, asked what he does there,
Says, "I've complaints against this pair."

Up to the monarch's throne they're brought;
The King is told why they've been caught.

He strokes his beard so old and grey,
And says, "What do the culprits say?"

At length the plane begins to descend, and, gliding towards a wide snowfield, it comes to rest before a great palace of solid ice, whose jagged pinnacles are soaring to the sky. Rupert and Algy are not allowed to get down. The snow man tucks one under each arm and strides towards the entrance. At the palace they are challenged by a fierce little sentry with a sharp spear, but the snow man is not afraid. "I have a complaint to make," he says, "I must see King Frost at once."

Marching through the palace, the two chums find themselves carried into a wide hall hung with icicles. On a throne sits King Frost in his robes. "Your Majesty," says the snow man solemnly, "these two miscreants have been caught in the act of causing wilful damage to a snow man. They would have destroyed me also but for your messenger's help. I have brought them to you for judgment." The King rises and gravely strokes his beard. "This is a serious crime," he says at length. "What have you two to say for yourselves?"

From *Rupert and King Frost*, 1940. Rupert is the only comic strip in which speech bubbles are not included in the pictures. The illustrator Alfred Bestall developed the classic format that can be read on four levels: pictures, page headers, verses and prose.

WHO IS RUPERT BEAR?

Rupert lives with his mother and father in a cottage in Nutwood. He is an only child, and has many chums with whom he gets into lots of adventures, but he is kind, brave and resourceful and always manages to return safely home. Rupert wears a red sweater and yellow checked trousers and a matching scarf. Originally drawn as a brown bear, his colour was changed to white to reduce printing costs, although he is brown on the covers of the annuals.

Geraldine McCaughrean
BELLEROPHON

"One heartbeat after Perseus the Hero struck the head from the Gorgon Medusa and stuffed it into a sack, two creatures were born. They escaped like foam from a bottle – a winged horse as white as cloud; a mortal man sheathed in golden armour. Pegasus the horse bolted into the wilds of the sky, the man into the wide world."

Geraldine clearly likes to challenge people (and herself). No one else had presented us with the extraordinary task of finding or creating a large white horse with wings. But Bellerophon needs Pegasus, and so we looked at a number of options. We seriously considered bringing a white horse into the Story Museum. We looked at possible mock-ups, and we thought about creating the image digitally. It is a tribute to the energy and enthusiasm with which Geraldine threw herself into the part that in the end we felt the spirit of the flying horse was captured by her essence and performance.
Cambridge Jones

WHO IS GERALDINE McCAUGHREAN?

Geraldine McCaughrean was born in London in 1951. As a child, she enjoyed reading, but loved writing even more as it allowed her to escape further into her imagination. After studying English literature at university she worked as a secretary, teacher, journalist and sub-editor, writing in her spare time. Gradually the hobby became the work she loves, which has resulted in over 160 books, 60 plays and a shelf of awards for her wide-ranging original fiction and vivid retellings of myths, legends and moments from history. In 2004, Geraldine won a national competition to write the sequel to *Peter Pan*, continuing the story of Peter, Wendy and the Lost Boys in *Peter Pan in Scarlet*.

Geraldine McCaughrean with her actress daughter Ailsa

Q & A

CAMBRIDGE JONES: Who is your character, and why did you choose him?

GERALDINE MCCAUGHREAN: My character is Bellerophon. Not because he is a role model exactly, because he's not. I didn't ever want to be a great killer of monsters. But the fact that he tamed Pegasus was my great draw to the man. This is why his story lodged in my young mind. He flew Pegasus to the top of Mount Olympus. And he was able to kill a Chimera, and I wasn't at the age of seven or eight. A lot of the gratification I got from the reading and writing which I was doing, even then, was that I could be all those things which I wasn't ever going to be. Apart from the obvious, that I was never going to be a man and I was never going to be Greek, and I was unlikely ever to tame Pegasus, I *could* be brave and I *could* defeat monsters!

CJ: Is there a favourite bit of the story?

GMcC: Yes, it's the gentlest bit of his whole violent story! It's where he sleeps in the temple and he wakes up and the golden bridle is beside him. And he dreams that what he has to do is go and find Pegasus and put this bridle on Pegasus, and then he will obtain the winged horse.

CJ: Do you remember when and how you first heard this story?

GMcC: No. In the local library was a corner called Myths and Legends, which was largely Greek myths and legends. And they were all presented in a rather educational way and invariably illustrated with pictures from Greek vases – with people throwing discuses – and really not terribly exciting. Greek myth books have come on an awful lot in the past forty years. So I just assimilated a whole lot of bits of Greek myth stories. What I did pick up was that this is one big patchwork quilt. Everything joins on to something else, and

I love that. Because Pegasus – and just possibly Bellerophon – are the children of Medusa. When her head was cut off by Perseus she was pregnant. She was pregnant with twins. If you talk to children in school about this and you say, "What is your idea of a hero?" it's Perseus and he's going to cut off the head of this hideous monster. But then you say, "But this hideous monster was in fact a very beautiful woman at one time and she is also pregnant with twins. Now do you think it's quite nice?" And you can actually turn the hero and villain around. And I love doing that, because the Greeks were terrified of women and monsters.

CJ: Why did you become a storyteller?

GMcC: I had to be a storyteller because I couldn't speak a coherent sentence when I was little: I was so, so shy. I couldn't talk to people. I found that if I wrote things down I could get to the end of the sentence. And then of course, what do children write? They write stories. So, when I was writing stories I discovered I could be anybody at all. And I chiefly wanted to be a horse, really, when I was little. I gather the Queen also wanted to be a horse when she was a child, so I'm not alone in it.

Five, six, up to about nine, I suppose, I was just horses, horses, horses. And writing, writing, writing. I used to meet up with my junior school teacher and she'd say, "Are you still writing stories about horses, dear?" Because whatever she *asked* us to write in creative English time, I just wrote a story about a horse! They were entirely for me. Later on I used to write stories and read them during playtime. That was more secondary school. I used to write episodes of TV series and read them in the break.

It would be nice to go back, but they were rubbish. You

see, my brother Neil was an all-round genius and could do everything, including painting and modelmaking and writing. And he got published when he was fourteen. So after that of course I was thinking, I want to get published, I want to write a book like Neil. But I wasn't like Neil, not in any way. I wasn't very bright. I wasn't very clever at school. The only thing I could do – did do – was write. And after I went to secondary school I even stopped getting praised for writing, just because I wasn't all-round clever.

CJ: That's fascinating. So school's version of writing has to fit into a certain box?

GMcC: It does, more now even than when I was at school. It has to have a function. Why are we learning to write? Why are we doing a story? Because it will teach us about phonemes and sub-clauses. No, that's not actually why. That's not why we read either. Why are we studying literature in school, telling children what it's about and what they're supposed to think about it, when the person that wrote it was asking questions? That's all literature ever was, it was saying, "What do you think about this?" The point of giving a book to a child is to ask, "What do you think about this?" It's the only time in school that you ever do. Who do you want to be? Do you think this is a good story? Does it teach you anything? Or is it just subversive? Does it make you want to go off and do wicked, heroic, dangerous, villainous things?

CJ: When did it occur to you that you could do this for a living?

GMcC: I suppose ultimately I knew it was the only thing I was good at. But I went out and got a proper job, because you have to be clever and you have to go to university and things like that to be a writer, don't you? And no one's going to take *me* seriously. So I just did it for a hobby.

I was a secretary and then I trained to be a teacher. I was so shy! I use to walk into a class of children and look at them and think, "Oh, they're all looking at me. Oh." And turn around and walk out again! That was just on teaching practice, so I knew very soon, I'm not going to be able to do that. I distinctly remember going to a lecturer at teacher training college and bursting into tears on his desk and saying, "I don't want to teach, I want to be a writer," and he said, "Well go on then! Why don't you?" And I was so taken aback. It was brilliant. And almost from that moment on it was, "All right, I will!"

WHO IS BELLEROPHON?

Bellerophon is a Greek mythical hero who appears in Homer's *Iliad*. Born from the throat of Medusa as she was killed, and banished for an accidental murder, he is then falsely accused of seducing the wife of King Proteus. Proteus sends Bellerophon to his father-in-law, King Iobates, carrying a tablet saying "Pray remove the bearer from this world: he attempted to violate my wife, your daughter." So Iobates sends Bellerophon on a dangerous quest to kill the Chimera, a fire-breathing, three-headed monster. For this, he is advised, he needs a winged horse. After taming Pegasus, Bellerophon succeeds in suffocating the monster with a block of molten lead and then in defeating the Solymi and the Amazons, both ferocious warriors. His reward is the hand of the King's daughter, Philonoe.

Bellerophon is happy but not satisfied. He decides to ride Pegasus to Mount Olympus to visit the gods. Zeus, angered by his presumption, sends a gadfly to sting the flying horse. Bellerophon is thrown and falls to earth, ending his days crippled and alone.

Bellerophon, like Icarus, is used to show the dangers of pride. Some say his story inspired the legend of Saint George and the Dragon, and, with its mention of "sad signs" scratched on a tablet, it contains Homer's only mention of writing, the first in Greek literature.

Bellerophon

THE MYTH OF PEGASUS AND BELLEROPHON

" The Oracle peered into Bellerophon's face, though one of her eyes seemed to be looking over his shoulder and into the Future. 'To defeat the Chimera, you will need the power of flight. Even the winged sandals the gods gave to Perseus the Hero would not be enough. *You* will need the winged horse Pegasus.'

The wind whistled and thunder clattered around the sky. Bellerophon felt the sound of the name like a bell tolling inside him, but could not imagine why.

'Catch the uncatchable?' he said. 'No one has ever ridden Pegasus.'

'Sleep in the Temple of Athena,' said the Oracle. 'If you are fortunate, the goddess may send you a dream.'

Picture trying to sleep: the floor hard, the night cold, thoughts galloping about your head. Is that the sound of dry leaves blowing across the floor, or the sandals of a goddess? Is that the banging of the door in the wind, or the Chimera scratching itself against the temple wall? Finally sleep came, silent as smoke, and dreams pillowed Bellerophon's head. He dreamed a white horse stood over him, its mane tumbling into his face. When it whinnied, Bellerophon woke with a start.

No horse. No goddess. No monster. But there on the temple floor lay a tangle of rope. On hands and knees he scurried over to it – the golden bridle that would grant him mastery over the legendary flying horse.

When Bellerophon saw Pegasus drinking from a spring pool, the heart in his chest bucked painfully, stung by wonder. Many had glimpsed the stallion in the sky or hurtling through a forest or silhouetted on a hill top, but no hunter or treasure-hunter had ever crept close enough to touch that silvery flank. So he fully expected the heels to kick up, the haunches to clench and for the horse to leap the pool and disappear into the distance. Pegasus simply looked at him – or rather the bridle in his hand – and allowed Bellerophon to walk closer. The wings stirred and opened – an awkward clutter of bone and muscle – until they covered both withers and flanks, from shoulder to tail. Where would a rider sit amid all those feathers? And how could Bellerophon hope to reach the snowy plateau of Pegasus's back?

For a long time, he stood facing the horse. He made no secret of the golden bridle: a horse is only bridled who consents to being ridden. When they looked into each other's eyes, all time dropped away, as if the world had yet to be created and the Past had yet to happen. It was as if both had once shared the same cramped stable-stall.

'May I?' said Bellerophon at last, holding out the bridle.

And Pegasus dipped his head into the noose.

It was not difficult in the least to find sitting space within the wings. Once astride that slender back, the rider was cradled by the wings, as a swan's cygnets are kept safe on her back. They flew.

Like a dolphin in a sunlit sea, Pegasus belonged in the aquamarine sky. Though his hooves galloped strenuously, the power of motion came from his immense wings. Such was his beauty that horses on the ground looked up from between their cart shafts, under their heavy panniers or the yoke of a plough and thought their own souls had broken free and made a bolt for freedom.

Bellerophon looked down on hills, valleys and fields, on beaches, reefs and islands, and laughed out loud for sheer joy. Not since the boy Icarus put on home-made wings and jumped off a window-sill had anyone glimpsed the earth like this. Icarus had plunged to his death, betrayed by his frail wings, but Pegasus's wings were tireless, and so was his loyalty. For it seemed as if both man and horse had been lacking something until the golden bridle bound them together.

For days they played together, like children, stooping on orchards, amid a noisy ruffling of feathers, so that Bellerophon could spear oranges off the trees, with his javelin. On such a beast he could have ridden to the frozen north, the sweltering south, the gates of dawn or the curtains of sunset... but he had sworn an oath to kill the Chimera, and in those days a promise was as unbreakable as a magic bridle. So away they cantered towards the lovely province of Lycia, now charred and mangled by the monster which had made the place its lair.

Even the legendary Perseus, armed and armoured by the gods, had given in to doubt as he approached the lair of the gorgon Medusa. But if Perseus had ever seen *the Chimera*, he would have wept like a child and run home to mummy. This creature was a hideous, unnatural mish-mash of animal parts and pieces. Its skull was a lion's head, orange-maned and snarling. Its body was a goat's – oh, not some farmyard nanny-goat, but a stocky, bullish Nubian so surefooted it could have climbed a cliff of glass. Its haunches were scaly, and dragged along behind them a massive, coiling tail. Still, men have killed snakes and lions and goats before, haven't they? So why had whole armies of men met their death in the jaws of the Chimera?

Because the roar that came from those lion jaws was the roar of a firestorm. A furnace burned within that outlandish body, so hot that fences charred and cornfields blazed as the beast passed by. Impossible to approach, impossible to trap, the Chimera had nothing to fear from puny mankind.

Bellerophon considered his options. He would fly out of the sun, so that the monster was unsighted! He would rain sword-blows on it from above when it was sleeping! He would poison its meat, or lure it into the sea to put out its flame! But the Chimera could swallow any poison. It never slept. It could turn the sea to steam, and scent any prey from ten leagues away. Even as Pegasus and Bellerophon flew high overhead, they could feel the heat from its fiery carcase scorch their skin."

From *Pride Comes Before a Fall: The story of Bellerophon* by Geraldine McCaughrean, 2014

Michael Morpurgo
MAGWITCH

" 'You get me a file.' He tilted me again.
'And you get me wittles.' He tilted me again.
'You bring 'em both to me.' He tilted me again.
'Or I'll have your heart and liver out.' "

Like several of our male authors, Michael was not an avid reader when young. He explained to me that he found books were hard work to get through and lacked the appeal of playing in the outdoors with other kids. This seems interesting to me on two levels: firstly, it is of course no accident that the Story Museum has focused its mission on stories rather than books, taking the story out of the realm of "classroom" and "homework" and putting it firmly in the realm of imagination and fun; and secondly, that one of the most successful storytellers of our age is as empowered and fuelled by his imagination fed on childhood play as he is from a scholarly digestion of letters and punctuation.

Cambridge Jones

WHO IS MICHAEL MORPURGO?

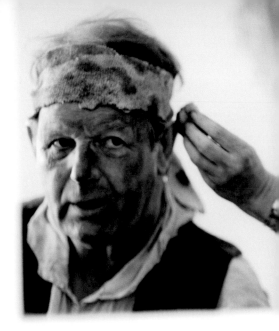

Michael Morpurgo went to school in London, Sussex and Canterbury, and studied English and French at London University. While working as a primary teacher he discovered his power to tell and write stories that children enjoy. In 1976, Michael and his wife Clare started Farms for City Children, a charity that gives inner-city children the chance to experience country life. Michael now divides his time between working on his Devon farm and writing stories. He has written over 100 novels, picture books, collections of short stories and libretti, including *War Horse*, *Private Peaceful* and *Kensuke's Kingdom*. Many have won prizes and been adapted for stage, film or television. Michael was the third Children's Laureate (2003–2005), a post he helped to create with the Poet Laureate, Ted Hughes.

Q & A

CAMBRIDGE JONES: Who is your character, and why did you choose him?

MICHAEL MORPURGO: I chose Magwitch, who is the convict in *Great Expectations* by Charles Dickens. I've chosen him for a lot of reasons. Because I love *Great Expectations*: I think it's one of the great books of the world. Because it was the first great classic, besides *Treasure Island*, that I ever managed to get through. I wasn't a great reader. I felt a great sense of achievement when I read it. And, although I'm sure I skipped pages, as you do when you're eleven and twelve, I remember feeling that I was in the landscape. I suspect it is that first scene that allows you into the book if you're a younger reader, that marvellous scene where Magwitch, through fear, persuades Pip to go and get him some food. That was the first time a book had my eyes really widened with fear.

CJ: Did you then start to read more?

MM: I have never read much. Not near as much as I should. I now read history, biography, poetry. I should read more fiction. I never got into the habit of it, which is why I'm so keen that kids should. Because I know it's something I missed.

I had a lovely start. My mother used to read to me, Kipling and Masefield, Wordsworth. I'd be lying in bed, she'd be sitting on my bed and for twenty minutes each evening she'd be reading to us. And she was an actress and she could speak and sing words beautifully. My brother Peter and myself, we just loved and adored stories and the music in the words.

But then we both went off to school. And of course, what happened at school then, happens sometimes at school now – I hope not quite so much – is that they formalised stories; it was the study of words and phrases and spelling and handwriting and testing and comprehension and more testing. And I learned to associate failing with words. I thought, "Books aren't for me. I'm going to go outside and play rugby." I don't think I've grown out of it completely now.

I learned to love reading again, and hearing stories, and hearing poems, when I was a teacher for eight years. I used to read to the children, recite poems to them, and I could see it meant a lot. And I could see it worked. I could see it was a magic for all of us. And I caught the magic myself then. And that's when I started telling my own stories, and then writing my own stories, and so I got back into stories.

CJ: Why did you become a storyteller?

MM: Well, there was a practical reason which I'm not going to disguise. The practical thing I had to do from three o'clock to half past three every afternoon was to keep thirty-five Year Sixes quiet. I'd been reading other people's stories and it had worked fine. If I put my heart and soul into the reading and it was a book I loved, it became a book they loved. Then I ran out of suitable books, and I could feel them shifting and looking out of the window and picking their noses, and it wasn't working. And I told my wife and she said, "Well, why don't you tell one of your own? You know, you're a pretty good liar! Make up a story and try it."

So I did. And I learned something very, very quickly in that one afternoon, which was if you believe in a story yourself, they're going to believe it. Even if it's quite an ordinary story. If you're telling it or you're writing it, you do it for yourself. You believe in it. You're fascinated by it. You become the characters in the story. And you can see the landscape, feel the landscape, smell the landscape. It has to become real for you, and then you can transfer that to the listener. And I think that's how my storytelling, which I don't really call writing, my story making, has always happened. It's because I'd been fascinated with a subject, got into a story myself.

Usually it's because it's a cause, something that I really object to, whether it's children being treated badly, or animals being sent off to war, or soldiers being shot for cowardice when they didn't have proper trials. There's quite a lot of that about it: things that make me cross. So I need to have a mission to write what I write, but then I just lose myself in the characters and tell it down on the page. But for me, not for anyone else. I have no child in my mind at all, no audience.

Great Expectations

by Charles Dickens

THE STORY

Pip, a young boy living in the marshes of Kent, is visiting the graveyard where his parents and brothers are buried. It's getting dark and windy when suddenly, from behind one of the gravestones, rears a hideous man with his legs in irons. Magwitch orders Pip to bring him food and a file, otherwise his "accomplice" will catch Pip and eat his heart...

Great Expectations is the thirteenth of fifteen novels written by Charles Dickens. Starting in the shadow of the prison ships and ending in a moonlit garden, it tells a powerful, twisting tale of wealth and poverty, love and rejection, good and evil. Originally serialised in Dickens's weekly magazine *All the Year Round*, it was published in three volumes in 1861, and has remained popular ever since. It has been frequently filmed and adapted for radio and television.

Dickens, like Pip in the story, had a turbulent childhood and was rejected by his first true love. He went on to become a successful journalist, performer and novelist, and throughout his life campaigned for the rights of children and the poor.

Above: Charles Dickens

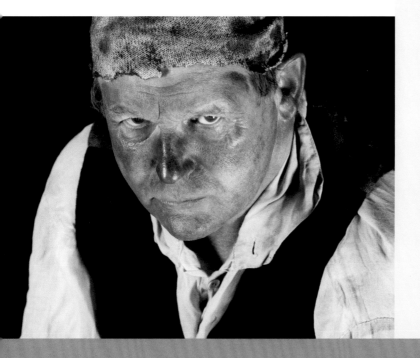

66 'Hold your noise!' cried a terrible voice, as a man started up from among the graves at the side of the church porch. 'Keep still, you little devil, or I'll cut your throat!'

A fearful man, all in coarse gray, with a great iron on his leg. A man with no hat, and with broken shoes, and with an old rag tied round his head. A man who had been soaked in water, and smothered in mud, and lamed by stones, and cut by flints, and stung by nettles, and torn by briars; who limped, and shivered, and glared and growled; and whose teeth chattered in his head as he seized me by the chin.

'Oh! Don't cut my throat, sir!' I pleaded in terror. 'Pray don't do it, sir.' "

From *Great Expectations*, Chapter I

WHO IS MAGWITCH?

Abel Magwitch appears little in *Great Expectations*, but is central to the story. The book opens with Magwitch, the escaped convict, threatening Pip in a graveyard. Pip helps him, but Magwitch is later recaptured and deported to Australia. It is not until many years later that we discover how he has influenced Pip's fortunes, having never forgotten the boy's small act of kindness.

Terry Pratchett
JUST WILLIAM

  " 'What have I just been saying, William?'

William sighed. That was the foolish sort of question that schoolmistresses were always asking. They ought to know themselves what they'd just been saying better than anyone. He never knew. Why were they always asking him?

He looked blank. Then:

'Was it anythin' about participles?' He remembered something vaguely about participles, but it mightn't have been today."

At the age of two and a half I was no longer to live with my real mother and father, and I moved to the family who lovingly and caringly brought me up from then on. I vividly remember the little cottage we moved into, with a stream running through the garden, and my new sister, and her toy horse which I threw into said stream. Imagine my surprise then, forty-plus years later, when I turn up at Terry's house and look across from his garden to see the very same cottage and stream. I had arrived early, so was able to chat with Terry and Rob (his right-hand man) about it all – very moving.

Cambridge Jones

WHO IS TERRY PRATCHETT?

T erry Pratchett was born in 1948 in Beaconsfield, Buckinghamshire, and credits his education to the Beaconsfield Public Library. At thirteen, his first short story, "The Hades Business", appeared in his school magazine: two years later it was published commercially.

Terry left school at seventeen to become a journalist with the Bucks Free Press, where he also wrote stories for the children's section under the name Uncle Jim. In 1968, when interviewing a director of Colin Smythe Ltd, a small publishing company, he mentioned he had written a manuscript. The company published *The Carpet People* in 1971, with Terry's illustrations, and later his first Discworld novel, a comic fantasy called *The Colour of Magic*.

In 1987, after finishing his fourth Discworld novel, *Mort*, Terry gave up his job with the Central Electricity Generating Board to write full-time. He has written 50 books, 39 of them set in Discworld, as well as short stories, plays, screenplays and non-fiction, won numerous awards, sold over 80 million volumes and been translated into 38 languages. He was knighted in 2009.

Q & A

CAMBRIDGE JONES: Who is your character, and why did you choose him?

TERRY PRATCHETT: I am William Brown, better known as "Just William". And "It's not fair." He always says things like "It's not fair," or "It stands to reason."

I chose him because his author was one of the best authors there ever has been for children. That was Richmal Crompton. A woman, though lots of people thought she was a man. Why Just William? I like his style. He never gave up, for one thing. He wouldn't back off if he thought he was right. Also, he had a lot of fun. He seemed to smash someone's window every week and it would be the slipper. And that seemed to have no effect on him whatsoever. And the way he spoke, and the way he reasoned; I recognised it as a way of speaking and reasoning that was not necessarily mine. The lady who wrote him was an absolute genius.

CJ: Do you remember when you first discovered him?

TP: My dad had kept a few of his books – so, when I found them. What boy would not want to be Just William? In those days, you have to remember this, we were more or less in the countryside, so the ethos of William Brown was in the air. We weren't quite as bad as he was, but we recognised this wasn't just a fantasy universe. For kids today, I suspect, it would be.

Richmal Crompton was excellent with words. But she could be acerbic to boot. I learned the word "acerbic" by looking it up, but realised much later in life: yes, she was acerbic. She didn't look down on children. Some of the words she used were ones that kids probably wouldn't know. But never mind, you'll find out later.

As soon as I got into reading, I was reading Richmal Crompton. It took a long time for me to get into reading. At Holts County Primary School, Mr H. W. Thame, the head teacher, reckoned that he could tell if a kid could go through to the 11-plus by how they could read at the age of six. And I couldn't read that well. In a way, I was a bit of a Just William. Trees. Sunshine. Things to get up to. And a dad who would tell me how to make things that I shouldn't be making. Because he, in a sense, egged me on to have the kind of life that he had when he was a boy. Although he had an air gun, which I didn't have. Thank goodness for that, because I'd have shot something! He'd take me walking and talking about things in the hedgerows and stuff.

But at the primary school, if you didn't make the grade, you went into what you might call "the bucket" (my term). You would be one of the kids that didn't pass the 11-plus. I think my mum found out about this, and she was a pushy mum, even before the phrase "pushy mum" had been created. And she went around looking for books for me to read. And my dad said, "Give him the *Just William* books," because he liked them when he was a kid. And I thought it was amazing! It was amazing how many school holidays you could have in one year; because it was always the holidays and it hardly ever rained on Just William.

I was actually learning, and friends of the family were digging into their attics for volumes of *Just William*. And I was going through all of them. And I found out "acerbic" and "sarcasm" and various other little words, and worked out later that that's exactly what Richmal Crompton was doing. I really loved her style.

CJ: Did it take you out of "the bucket"?

TP: Well. William possibly – but the one that got me right to the tip of the bucket and out was *The Wind in the Willows*. I remember what happened was, my mum thought, I've got to get him writing. Being that kind of woman, she said, "Look, I'll give you a penny per page finished correctly." The fourth book was *Wind in the Willows*. After that, she could save her money. Because that is a *magnificent* book. I think it's the one that made me want to be a writer because you could turn the world upside down. I know how big a mole is and how big a rat is and how big a toad is. And I'm pretty certain a toad cannot actually drive a car, even if you've got big pedals. *The Wind in the Willows* was when I thought, hang on, *this is how you can lie and nobody minds.*

CJ: And why did you become a storyteller?

TP: Because I realised that you could tell lies, and change the world a bit. Once I was reading, and went on reading, somehow the fact that I was reading made me read better at school. Once I'd found Beaconsfield Public Library (which ought to have a little shrine up there now), my school work went up. And in the primary school, now that's the interesting thing, the headmaster did me a little bit of a favour: he put me down. Up to that point, I'd been kind of halfway up the ladder, doing enough to get along. And suddenly half the kids, the kids that were going to do the 11-plus, were the sheep. And I was put among the goats, and the goats were going to go to the secondary modern. Everyone knew that. Frankly, I was brighter than them.

I went to something called High Wycombe Technical High School, which was kind of a hybrid. You could do woodwork, because it was High Wycombe and that was a furniture town in those days. I didn't like it at all and I didn't

like the head teacher. Again, all the teachers I went up against actually ended up making my future more golden. I was by then something like Just William, asking too many questions, saying, "Why not?", slightly bolshy. Possibly because of *Wind in the Willows*. "Do you realise that the horse that pulls the caravan has no name and no voice?" There was something inside me that thought "Solidarity, Brothers!"

At High Wycombe, I did enough to get along. And then one day we had a supply teacher and she, not knowing what to get us to do, told us to write a short story. And I wrote something which I called "The Hades Business" where – ahead of its time in a way, now I look at it – the vocabulary that I used was not what a child my age would normally be using. It's about how Satan, realising that hell is not very popular any more, gets in someone who can actually make going to hell seem a good experience. Fortunately, the teacher showed it to the Head of English and he put it in the school magazine and the kids loved it. The headmaster did not, which made it even better.

CJ: And that's the beginning of you starting to write?

TP: Well, the thing is the applause of the mob, if you see what I mean. The kids liked it. And indeed, my old school still has a copy of it enshrined in a plastic thing.

I like science fiction: science fiction is incredibly good for kids. And not just because I sometimes do it! Once upon a time people would say you shouldn't tell kids fairy stories because it tells them there are monsters, and G. K. Chesterton (I'm quoting him now) said, "Children already know there are monsters. Fairy stories tell them that monsters can be killed." Chesterton was another cornerstone for me.

There were three science fiction books produced, I think every other week, by the same editor, John Carnell. And I sent my short story off to him. And he wrote back and said it needs tweaking and he told me what to tweak. And he paid me money. Money!

CJ: How old would you have been?

TP: Middle teens. In the way of science fiction in those days, a guy would buy anything he thought was good. It could be a long time before it came out. He'd pick it up: "How long is this one? Have we got enough space for this one?" This was my famous first sale.

CJ: Wonderful.

TP: No, I should have had it harder. I think I would have been better.

Just William

by Richmal Crompton

WHO IS JUST WILLIAM?

William Brown is eleven years old and likes white rats, boiled sweets and adventures out of doors. With his friends Ginger, Henry and Douglas – "the Outlaws" – and mongrel dog, Jumble, William harasses his unfortunate family and neighbours with a series of schemes that start well but invariably go awry. Whether he's wrecking his big brother's love life or throwing a wild party in his parents' absence, due to "misunderstanding a double negative", the consequences are always comical. He's scruffy, reckless and irrepressible and has been making readers laugh for over 90 years.

THE STORY

William goes to the pictures. William gets a job as a servant. William puts on an animal show. William and his friends look after a baby. William is forced to be a page at his cousin's wedding. But wherever William goes, trouble follows...

Just William is the first of 38 William Brown books, written by Richmal Crompton over a period of fifty years. Richmal Crompton Lamburn was born in Bury, Lancashire, in 1890, the second daughter of a clergyman schoolmaster. The name "Richmal", combining Richard and Mary, had been in her mother's family since the 1700s.

Crompton went to St Elphin's boarding school, won a scholarship to Royal Holloway College, London and returned to St Elphin's in 1914 as a classics mistress, later moving to Bromley High School, where she started to write short stories. One, featuring a mischievous schoolboy, William Brown, was published in *Home*, a magazine for ladies, and became a monthly series. In 1922, two collections of the stories were published as *Just William* and *More William*, and in 1923, when Crompton lost the use of her right leg following an attack of polio, she decided to give up teaching and write full-time. Crompton preferred to write adult novels, but none surpassed the huge popularity of her William stories, which have sold over 12 million books and been successfully translated to radio, television and film.

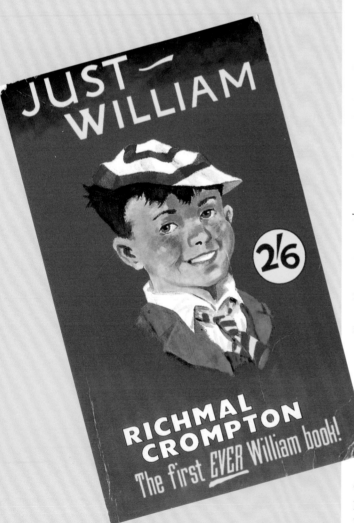

JUST WILLIAM

2/6

RICHMAL CROMPTON
The first *EVER* William book!

 Mr. Brown rose with the air of a man goaded beyond endurance.

'Where *is* William!' he said shortly.

'I don't know, but I thought I heard him go upstairs some time ago.'

William *was* upstairs. For the last twenty minutes he had been happily and quietly engaged upon his bedroom door with a lighted taper in one hand and penknife in the other. There was no doubt about it. By successful experiment he had proved that that was the way you got old paint off. When Mr Brown came upstairs he had entirely stripped one panel of its paint.

✺ ✺ ✺

An hour later William sat in the back garden on an upturned box sucking, with a certain dogged defiance, the last and dirtiest of the Gooseberry Eyes. Sadly he reviewed the day. It had not been a success. His generosity to the little girl next door had been miscon- strued into an attempt upon her life, his efforts to help on his only sister's love affair had been painfully misunderstood, lastly because (among other things) he had discovered a perfectly scientific method of removing old paint, he had been brutally assaulted by a violent and unreasonable parent. Suddenly William began to wonder if his father drank."

From *Just William*, Chapter 1

Above: Richmal Crompton

Philip Pullman
LONG JOHN SILVER

"His left leg was cut off close by the hip,
and under the left shoulder he carried
a crutch, which he managed with wonderful
dexterity, hopping about upon it like a bird.
He was very tall and strong, with a face
as big as a ham – plain and pale,
but intelligent and smiling."

One of the most exciting aspects of working on this project for the Story Museum has been the transformative nature of the process. Without fail we take erudite and grown-up writers and turn them into little children again. In Philip's case this was even more pronounced than normal. He'd not been well and yet valiantly came to the shoot anyway. It was clearly an effort for him even to get up the many flights of stairs. Yet after a little make-up and a costume from the National Theatre we had one of the most agile, loud and spirited Long John Silvers you are ever likely to meet. I salute him and his commitment.

Cambridge Jones

WHO IS PHILIP PULLMAN?

Philip Pullman grew up in England, Zimbabwe, Australia and Wales. As a child he loved roaming outdoors and reading comics, especially *Superman* and *Batman*. When he was eleven he had an English teacher, Miss Enid Jones, who so inspired him that he still sends her copies of all his books.

Philip studied English at Oxford and began his first novel the day after his final exams. He worked for twelve years as a teacher, delighting his pupils by telling myths and legends and creating thrilling plays. Later he trained teachers, encouraging them to tell stories and make learning fun. He has written over 30 books, graphic novels and plays, and is best known for *His Dark Materials*, an epic struggle across parallel universes. *The Amber Spyglass*, the second book in the series, made history by becoming the first children's book to win the Whitbread Book of the Year Award.

Q & A

CAMBRIDGE JONES: Who is your character, and why did you choose him?

PHILIP PULLMAN: I'm dressed as Long John Silver, and he's one of my favourite characters in the whole of literature, not just in the whole of children's literature. He's such a dramatic, attractive, exciting character. Whenever he turns up in the story of *Treasure Island*, you know there's going to be some skulduggery going on, some bloodshed, or some fighting, or some treachery.

He's also immensely charming: he can charm anyone. He has a very easy, free, friendly, delightful manner. He's jokey, he's funny. But of course that goes with being the double-dyed rogue.

The character, of course, really only lives in the words of Robert Louis Stevenson on the page. That is until the various depictions of Long John Silver in the cinema, of which the most famous is, I suppose, Robert Newton in the film in 1951, "Har-HARRRR, Jim lad," which was caricatured by a great many people. But it's Stevenson's own wonderful writing that brings him to life. To conceive of a character like this, to have him walk into your story, is the greatest gift, it's the most wonderful thing to happen. And he must have chuckled. He must have rubbed his hands together with glee, must have walked up and down with delight when he thought of Long John Silver.

CJ: Why did you become a storyteller?

PP: I became a storyteller because I love stories so much I couldn't leave them alone. I read stories, I thought about stories, I told stories to my friends and to my brother when we were very young. I wanted to grow up and be a writer because that's what writers did, they told stories. I've been really lucky in fulfilling that childhood ambition.

There were several stages in my becoming a writer. One was, as quite a young child, I used to make up stories and tell them. Then, later on, occasionally, we had the chance of writing stories at school. This is a very long time ago, when we didn't do creative writing at school, there was no such exciting thing as that. We did essays. "What I did in the holidays" or dull stuff like that. But occasionally, once or twice a year, the English teacher would let us write a story and I threw myself into it with great gusto.

Then I grew up and I did English A-level, and I went to university and studied English literature. During which time I thought I'd be a poet as I liked writing poetry. But I quite quickly realised I wasn't very good at that. But the day after I finished my final exams at Oxford, I started my first novel. And I've been writing novels ever since. Sometimes it's hard and sometimes it's easy, but it's the only thing I want to do. Still, after fifty years or whatever it is.

Treasure Island

by Robert Louis Stevenson

THE STORY

Jim Hawkins, our young narrator, lives at his parents' inn, The Admiral Benbow, near Bristol, England. Some sinister strangers arrive and hand a curse in the form of a "black spot" to one of the guests, an old sailor named Billy Bones. That night Billy dies. Inside his battered sea chest Jim finds a treasure map of a faraway island. The local doctor and squire plan a voyage to find the treasure and hire Jim as their cabin boy. But trouble begins when one of Billy's old shipmates, Long John Silver, joins the crew as the ship's cook...

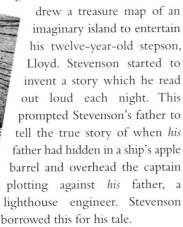

Treasure Island was born one chilly September morning when Robert Louis Stevenson drew a treasure map of an imaginary island to entertain his twelve-year-old stepson, Lloyd. Stevenson started to invent a story which he read out loud each night. This prompted Stevenson's father to tell the true story of when *his* father had hidden in a ship's apple barrel and overhead the captain plotting against *his* father, a lighthouse engineer. Stevenson borrowed this for his tale.

Originally serialised in 1883 in *Young Folks* magazine, *Treasure Island* quickly became a children's classic. Thanks to Robert Louis Stevenson, we now associate pirates with black spots, tropical islands and treasure maps marked with an X. The adventure has inspired many sequels and prequels as well as games and amusement park rides.

WHO IS LONG JOHN SILVER?

Also known as the Sea Cook and Barbecue, Long John Silver is the lovable rogue at the heart of *Treasure Island*. Charming and friendly, yet ruthless and scheming, he is ready to change sides when it suits him and will let nothing stand in his way in his quest for treasure. When J. M. Barrie, the author of *Peter Pan*, wanted children to fear Peter Pan's enemy, Captain Hook, he had only to say, "He is the only man of whom Barbecue was afraid." Yet most children would agree that Long John Silver is far scarier, and like him all the more for it.

"Now, just after sundown, when all my work was over, and I was on my way to my berth, it occurred to me that I should like an apple. I ran on deck. The watch was all forward looking out for the island. The man at the helm was watching the luff of the sail, and whistling away gently to himself; and that was the only sound excepting the swish of the sea against the bows and around the sides of the ship.

In I got bodily into the apple barrel, and found there was scarce an apple left; but, sitting down there in the dark, what with the sound of the waters and the rocking movement of the ship, I had either fallen asleep, or was on the point of doing so, when a heavy man sat down with rather a clash close by. The barrel shook as he leaned his shoulders against it, and I was just about to jump up when the man began to speak. It was Silver's voice, and, before I had heard a dozen words, I would not have shown myself for the world, but lay there trembling and listening, in the extreme of fear and curiosity; for from these dozen words I understood that the lives of all the honest men aboard depended upon me alone."

From *Treasure Island*, Chapter 10

Michael Rosen
TILL EULENSPIEGEL

"Till Eulenspiegel.

Till Owlyglass.

The wickedest trickster in Germany.

The worst boy the world has ever known,

who grew to be even worse than worst..."

on't throw fruit at a computer. My whole family will often recite these and other words from Michael's wonderful canon. It's only after spending a bit of time with him that I start to realise what a unique ability he has. Perhaps more than anyone we met on this odyssey through the world of storytellers he has the ability to synthesise the world view of an eight- or ten-year-old with the intellectual rigour and profundity of any of our academic philosophers or theorists. What's more, he loves doing it. Connecting thoughts. Mining words. Surfing phrases. Michael has a talent for storytelling for sure, but I suspect he also has a talent for living.

Cambridge Jones

WHO IS MICHAEL ROSEN?

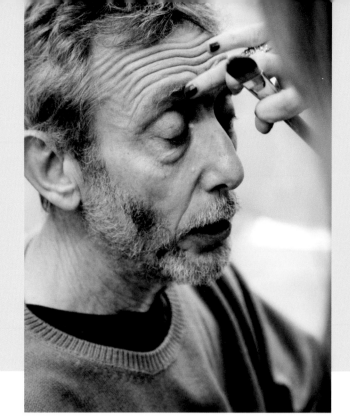

Michael Rosen is a poet, performer, broadcaster, writer and academic. Both his parents were teachers, and he grew up in Harrow, Middlesex, surrounded by stories, jokes and songs. When he left school he studied medicine, then swapped to English at Oxford University, becoming heavily involved in student drama. After two years at the BBC he started writing poetry for children, publishing *Mind Your Own Business* in 1974. Since then he has worked on over 140 books for readers of all ages, including non-fiction, novels, picture books, anthologies and retellings of classics and world stories, as well as collections of poetry. Michael has won numerous prizes and awards, was Children's Laureate (2007–2009) and the Story Museum's first Curator of Stories (2011–2013).

Q & A

CAMBRIDGE JONES: Who was your favourite childhood story character?

MICHAEL ROSEN: Without doubt, Till Eulenspiegel. Now, strangely, Till Eulenspiegel is not very well known in Britain, but if you were German I wouldn't really have to say anything else. It would be like saying Robin Hood.

He is a trickster, rogue, jester figure, and he played jokes on everybody almost from the time he was born. The first story you read about him is how he got baptised three times in one day. It finishes with his death, and he's even playing tricks after he's died. So it's a wonderful story cycle where he plays tricks on local farmers, and then on some robbers, and then he goes to the town and plays tricks on the baker, and he plays tricks on people selling things in the market. And then he goes up a level and he starts playing tricks on the petty princes. And he even gets as far as visiting the Pope and then playing tricks on the great scholars of the day.

He's still playing tricks on his deathbed, on the priest who is greedy and wants to get some money off him and ends up with his hand stuck in the chamber pot. My favourite is when he's just about to be hanged for having tricked all the weavers or the cobblers of a whole part of Germany! But he asks for a last boon, because it says in the town statutes that anybody who is hanged is allowed his last boon. He says, "My last boon is that every one of you, the mayor and the aldermen, will come to my grave after I'm dead and kiss my bum three times before breakfast." It's full of stuff like that. He's a wonderful, bawdy, crude trickster figure.

CJ: Why do stories matter to you in your work and life?

MR: I think stories are the means by which we carry most of the things we know. No matter how theoretical we get or how abstract we get, in order to understand things, we tie them to narrative. Sometimes we don't even recognise things

as narrative. If I say, "A bird in the hand is worth two in the bush," people will say, "That's not narrative. That's a proverb." But I have in fact painted a picture, and that proverb is embedded in a story. You can see somebody standing there with a bird in his hand, which we can assume he's going to eat, let's say he's a poacher or something like that (see, I'm already telling the story), but there's two in the bush and he's thinking, "I'm not going to go for those two, I'll keep the one I've got." So you can immediately tell the story. Proverbs are a way of carrying wisdom, but they're embedded in narrative.

Quite a lot of poetry is, if you like, the little frozen moment in a narrative. In the way that musicals freeze the moment when the lead male falls in love, or not in love! You can guess the hinterland.

Each time you find a maths equation, $x = 2y + $ whatever, if you step back a bit, x is representing something and y is representing something. If you're an engineer calculating something the tunnel goes through, well, there's the narrative. And you can go on and on.

You watch David Attenborough. You watch Patrick Moore. Watch any of these people trying to explain the world to us. They tell stories. The metamorphoses of butterflies and so on, those are life stories.

Stories are the way, in the end, I think we come to understand pretty well everything. You can go through procedures without narrative. A lot of my maths is like that, I just go through a procedure without having really any idea what I'm doing. But if you really want to understand things and make them your own, pretty nearly always, I wouldn't say absolutely always, you relate to events and things that are in some kind of chronological sequence, with characters that you can understand and recognise. I know it sounds trite, but I'd say narrative and story are, in the end, everything.

Till Eulenspiegel

THE STORY

Till Eulenspiegel is a character from German folklore, who was also known in Denmark, the Low Countries (nowadays Belgium and the Netherlands), Poland and Italy. The earliest written version of his pranks is an anonymous collection of 95 tales printed in about 1500 to "create a happy feeling in hard times". The stories have survived in music, film, dance, theatre and literature, and there are statues and monuments to him in Germany, as well as a stone that claims to mark his grave.

There are many variations of the Till Eulenspiegel story about the painting that cannot be seen if you are a liar, or stupid, or illegitimate, including one made famous by Hans Christian Andersen as "The Emperor's New Clothes". See overleaf for our version by Neill Cameron.

WHO IS TILL EULENSPIEGEL?

Till Eulenspiegel is a practical joker who delights in wordplay and often tricks people by following their instructions literally. So, when the king asks for the best horseshoes, Till annoys him by making them out of gold. His name means "owl" (*eulen*) and "mirror" (*spiegel*), perhaps because he holds up a "wise mirror" to reflect people's foolishness and greed. One story tells how Till Owlyglass, as he is known in English, would scrawl a picture of an owl and mirror above a door-way after a successful prank.

TILL EULENSPIEGEL AND THE POTENTATE'S PORTRAIT

Katherine Rundell
A WILD THING

"And when he came to the place where the wild things are
they roared their terrible roars and gnashed their terrible teeth
and rolled their terrible eyes and showed their terrible claws"

Katherine is an intriguing enigma to me. Rather like one of her characters sneaking across the roof tops, she sneaked into my life, charmed and entranced me, and then crept off again into the night. Such a beguiling mix of academic, dancer, diplomat and more. All I can really say is that she was great fun to work with, moves like a dream and was a truly wonderful Wild Thing.

Cambridge Jones

WHO IS KATHERINE RUNDELL?

Katherine Rundell studied English at Oxford University and in 2008 became a Fellow of All Souls College, where she researches seventeenth-century poetry and writes novels for children and adults. *The Girl Savage* was inspired by her beloved Zimbabwe, and *Rooftoppers* by summers working in Paris and nights trespassing on the roofs of Oxford colleges. Katherine keeps a tightrope in her study and walks it every day; she has her best ideas while doing handstands.

Q & A

CAMBRIDGE JONES: So, Katherine, who is your character, and why did you choose it?

KATHERINE RUNDELL: I am a Wild Thing from *Where the Wild Things Are* and I chose to be one because the book seemed to me closest to what it's really like to be a child. And because that opening line of *Where the Wild Things Are* – "The night Max wore his wolf suit and made mischief of one kind" – is one of the most extraordinary lines, and the tingles run down your finger-tips, along your spine, all the way down to your toes. It's just the most beautiful book I think I've read.

I think the best scene is when Max has reached the wild island and all the wild creatures have come and gathered around him and it says, "Let the wild rumpus start", which is the closest thing to heaven you get in literature.

CJ: Why did you become a storyteller?

KR: I knew I wanted to be a writer since I knew that it was a job. But storytelling has drawn me because it's for young people, and really good books can crowbar the world open for them. There's a critic who says poetry is there "to add to the available stock of reality", and I think the point of story-telling is to add to the available stock of joy or magic.

I think I was about four when I realised in a sudden moment of revelation that the books that were being read to me were written by people, that they hadn't arrived organically in the same way that fruit does, and that seemed to me just the best job there could be! To imagine a thing and to make it as close to reality as possible! That seemed pretty great.

I wrote my first book when I was six and it was called "Sally's Surprise" and it was a present for my father. The surprise was that there was no plot. Surprise! She wakes up and she goes to the swimming pool and then she goes to bed. But I remember thinking, "I've begun my route to stardom!"

CJ: When did you find out about the author of any book, as opposed to just taking what they've written?

KR: My generation didn't have Google: we still had AOL dial-up. So finding out about authors would have been some-thing that came from your teachers, perhaps quite small snippets of information like that Sendak was this ex-traordinary, slightly madcap figure who wrote beautiful letters in return to his fans and said some unrepeatable rude things about Salman Rushdie. I found that out at about ten, that he was a very charming misanthrope. But authors never interested me as much as their books did. I imagine that's slightly different now that every author has a web page.

CJ: At what point did you move from thinking "I want to do this" to "I'm writing a book and it's going to be published"?

KR: It hasn't happened yet! OK, OK, I remember this really vividly... It was the day after I turned 21, and I had exactly a month before I started a job, so I thought, "I'm going to write a book: if it fails totally I won't have wasted more than a month." I was trying to lower the stakes, to make it a less presumptuous act. Even now, when I write something it astonishes me that people will publish it. I feel like I'm pulling off the most almighty con.

Where the Wild Things Are

by Maurice Sendak

THE STORY

One day Max wears his wolfsuit and makes mischief. He is sent to bed without any supper. That night, a forest grows in his room, and vines, and an ocean, and a boat, so he sails away to the place where the wild things are. The wild things are fierce, but Max is fiercer: he tames them with a magic trick and becomes their king. But Max is lonely, and wants to be where someone loves him best of all...

Where the Wild Things Are is a children's picture book by American writer and illustrator Maurice Sendak which has sold over 20 million copies since its publication in 1963. Its 18 illustrations and 338 words revolutionised picture book publishing and have been adapted into animations, an opera and a live-action film.

Born in Brooklyn in 1928 to Polish-Jewish parents, Sendak's childhood was shaped by the deaths in the Holocaust of most of his extended family. He was a sickly child and spent much of his time reading and drawing, landing a part-time job creating comics while still at high school. His artistic skills were spotted by the famous New York toy store, F. A. O. Schwarz, which employed him as a window-dresser while he studied art for three years. After illustrating others' books, Sendak began to illustrate his own, vowing that his stories would reflect real life, not just "sunshine and rainbows". During his long career, he produced more than 50 books, including *In the Night Kitchen* and *Outside Over There*, as well as television programmes and designs for operas and musicals. Famously grumpy, he nevertheless always answered children's letters, once describing how charmed he'd been by a little boy who so loved his original drawing of a Wild Thing that he ate it.

WHAT IS A WILD THING?

Where the Wild Things Are began as "Where the Wild Horses Are", but Sendak discovered he couldn't draw horses. His editor asked what he could draw. "Things," he replied, and "things" he drew. The things were inspired by his childhood memories of his relatives: "They were unkempt; their teeth were horrifying. Hair unraveling out of their noses." In the book they are unnamed, but they were given names in the 2009 movie directed by Spike Jonze.

Holly Smale
THE WHITE WITCH

> 66 'She isn't a real queen at all,' answered Lucy; 'she's a horrible witch, the White Witch. Everyone – all the wood people – hate her. She has made an enchantment over the whole country so that it is always winter and never Christmas.'"

It was Holly's birthday when we met, and she had very kindly agreed to do the shoot before going on to celebrate later in the day. That is all I can tell you! She cast a spell on me from the moment that she put on her White Witch costume that left me speechless, such was her power and beauty. It's a miracle we got any photos out of the session at all. I was truly mesmerised.

Cambridge Jones

WHO IS HOLLY SMALE?

Holly Smale was born in 1981, and fell in love with writing at the age of five. She claims to have been a shy and slightly geeky girl who spent most of her school years hiding in the changing room toilets. At fifteen she was unexpectedly spotted by a top London modelling agency and hoped the work would lead to exotic travel. It didn't, although she did find other ways of living in Japan and Nepal and exploring the world. By the time she had left Bristol University with a BA in English literature and an MA in Shakespeare, Holly had given up modelling and decided to become a writer. Her first books, *Geek Girl* and *Model Misfit*, were published to rave reviews.

Q & A

CAMBRIDGE JONES: Which character have you chosen, and why?

HOLLY SMALE: I am Jadis, the White Witch of Narnia, and I chose her because *The Lion, the Witch and the Wardrobe* was one of my favourite books as a child. It had a massive impact on me. Jadis was terrifying, but really compelling. I felt sympathy with Edmund, because I would have got up on the chair next to her, and I wanted the Turkish Delight. I used to make my mum go and buy me Turkish Delight so I could eat it while reading the book and experience it on every level! The Queen was such a horrible lady, but so strong, and I found that incredibly appealing. There's something biting and witty about her. I would have liked it if she was a little more rounded-out. But because she's a representation of Satan, she isn't. You're supposed to hate her. But I was always intrigued.

CJ: Do you remember what age you were when you got into the Narnia books?

HS: Probably about seven. I was too young to see any religious narratives: I didn't see that until I was in my teens. I read them purely as stories. So it was a bit of a shock when I realised they might have another meaning. I have to focus on not thinking about that level, because for me it mars the story slightly. But as a child, it was magical.

CJ: And can I ask how you became a storyteller?

HS: The first book I remember falling in love with was *The Enchanted Wood*, when I was about four, and I became so obsessed with it that I used to carry it around and had fights with my mum about being able to read it at the dinner table. We came to a compromise, where I would be able to touch it with one finger while I ate dinner with the other hand! Because it wasn't just a book any more, it became a portal, and I suddenly realised what it was like to be at the dinner table but not at the dinner table at the same time. It was about the escapism, the magic of being able to leave where you are and be with other people in other places.

From that point on I was pretty much dedicated to stories. My childhood was quite a lonely one, partly because I found books more interesting than people. I was never a passive reader. The minute I finished *The Enchanted Wood* I got my mum to buy me loads of paper and I started to scribble. Occasionally I'd give people little poems as birthday presents, but generally my writing stayed secret until I was 25. I was working in a PR agency and didn't enjoy it. I remember someone said, "I really want to be a writer," and I was like, "Yeah, me too! And what I don't want to be for the rest of my life is someone who tells people that they want to be a writer, so I'm going to just do it and stop hiding stuff."

The book I got published first was the second book I had written. The first was rubbish! Even now I use "air quotes" when I say, "I'm a writer." It feels quite arrogant to claim that you make up stories for a living!

The Lion, the Witch and the Wardrobe

by C. S. Lewis

" 'Answer me, once and for all, or I shall lose my patience. Are you human?'

'Yes, your Majesty,' said Edmund.

'And how, pray, did you come to enter my dominions?'

'Please your Majesty, I came through the wardrobe.'

'A wardrobe? What do you mean?'

'I – I opened a door and just found myself here, your Majesty,' said Edmund.

'Ha!' said the Queen, speaking more to herself than to him. 'A door. A door from the world of men! I have heard of such things. This may wreck all. But he is only one, and he is easily dealt with.'

As she spoke these words she rose from her seat and looked Edmund full in the face, her eyes flaming; at the same moment she raised her wand. Edmund felt sure that she was going to do something dreadful but he seemed unable to move. Then, just as he gave himself up for lost, she appeared to change her mind.

'My poor child,' she said in quite a different voice, 'how cold you look! Come and sit with me here on the sledge and I will put my mantle round you and we will talk.'

Edmund did not like this arrangement at all but he dared not disobey; he stepped on to the sledge and sat at her feet, and she put a fold of her fur mantle round him and tucked it well in.

'Perhaps something hot to drink?' said the Queen.

'Should you like that?' "

From *The Lion, the Witch and the Wardrobe*, Chapter Four

WHO IS THE WHITE WITCH?

Jadis is a beautiful and cruel sorceress, seven feet tall, with a magic wand that can turn living creatures to stone. In *The Magician's Nephew*, which was written later than *The Lion, the Witch and the Wardrobe*, but is set at the creation of Narnia 1,000 years earlier, we learn that Jadis is the last Queen of a world called Charn, which she has destroyed in order to defeat her sister. In Narnia she eats the Fruit of Everlasting Life, which makes her immortal but turns her skin completely white. It is thought that C. S. Lewis took her name from the French word *jadis* meaning "long ago", which was traditionally used to begin stories.

THE STORY

The four Pevensie children are sent to live at their uncle's country house. One rainy day, Lucy, the youngest, climbs into a wardrobe and finds herself in a mysterious snowy world. There she meets a faun who tells her that she is in Narnia, which has been enchanted by a wicked sorceress. When Lucy returns and tells her siblings, they refuse to believe her. But then her brother Edmund finds his way through the wardrobe and falls under the spell of the evil White Witch...

The Lion, the Witch and the Wardrobe is the first children's book by the academic and author Clive Staples Lewis. Born in Belfast in 1898, Lewis loved writing stories with his brother Warren, and became interested in Celtic and Norse literature. He studied classics and English literature at Oxford, and became a professor there and later at Cambridge. Lewis thought deeply about religion and became internationally famous for his religious books and radio broadcasts.

In September 1939, at the start of the Second World War, three children were evacuated to Lewis's home and he decided to write a fairy story with a Christian theme. He started with an image that had popped into his head many years earlier, of a faun carrying parcels and an umbrella through a snowy wood. The book became popular and, with the encouragement of his friend J. R. R. Tolkien, and others in their writers' group, the Inklings, Lewis wrote six more *Chronicles of Narnia*. The series has inspired many other children's fantasy authors and numerous adaptations.

Benjamin Zephaniah
ANANSI THE SPIDER

"Once, there were no stories in the world.
Anansi the Spider Man decided that he
would like to buy some. So he climbed to
the top of the very tallest mountain,
and shouted up at the sky."

I have worked with Benjamin several times in
my career. Once when I was a student and we
wanted him on the cover of our student magazine
Isis (he was very cool and living with his dub band
in Handsworth), with all the requisite Rasta
accoutrements. Then again in East London when he
was suffering greatly from racist attacks and couldn't
reveal his address to anyone for fear of such an attack.
Now I arrive at the door of his university office and
see "Professor Benjamin Zephaniah" written in smart
letters on the door. "You've come up in the world,"
I say teasingly, but am greeted with a slightly worried,
"Have I? I hope not." This is a man who was put
amongst us to enlighten and help others – not to rise
above them. My flattery was wasted if not confusing.
And what a spider he makes!
Cambridge Jones

WHO IS BENJAMIN ZEPHANIAH?

Benjamin Zephaniah describes himself as a poet, writer, lyricist, musician and troublemaker. The son of a Barbadian postman and a Jamaican nurse, he grew up in the Handsworth district of Birmingham, which he regards as the Jamaican capital of Europe. Benjamin is dyslexic and left school at thirteen unable to read or write. But he had already started to perform his own poetry, and by the time he was fifteen had developed a local reputation for tackling social issues with humour. When he was 22 he moved to London, determined to make poetry relevant and accessible. He performed his dub (reggae) poems at dances and demonstrations, on stage and television, and injected new life into the British poetry scene.

Benjamin's collection of poems, *Pen Rhythm*, was published in 1980, the first of nearly 30 poetry books, novels and plays, including *Talking Turkeys*, poems for children, and the teen novel *Refugee Boy*. Benjamin is Professor of Poetry and Writing at Brunel University and travels the world performing and campaigning on a range of social issues. He is a passionate vegan, practitioner of martial arts and football supporter, and was a friend of the late South African president, Nelson Mandela.

Keeper of stories
Spinner of tales
Cunning Anansi
The original spider man

Q&A

CAMBRIDGE JONES:
So who is your character, and why did you choose him?

BENJAMIN ZEPHANIAH:
My character is Anansi. Anansi is this spider that kind of has a wisdom all of his own. He gets himself in trouble but always manages to find a way out. He was really popular in Jamaica. I was born in England, but my mother was from Jamaica, so I heard lots of Anansi stories. But actually, originally, he originated in West Africa. And I just have real

vivid memories of sometimes, when something would happen to me and my mother would say to me, "You know Anansi Spider? He was in this position and you know what he did?" And she'd tell me the Anansi story. There was a whole lot of people who think that Anansi should stay as this mythical character, shouldn't be written down, shouldn't be depicted. But I actually think it's good to bring him to life, especially in this modern age.

There's a story for almost every situation and even if there's not a story, if you understand a character, you can make up the story. So, you know, my mother would say, "What would Anansi do now?" For example, let's just say Anansi stole some food because he was hungry, and Anansi was a suspect. I'm making this up off the top of my head now! Anansi would consider his options. Of course, Anansi wouldn't want to go to Spider Jail. So Anansi would grow some food, put it back and go and apologise. Something like that. It was always a very simple story. He'd find a clever way out. So it was either as it was or better than it was, and he could walk away and say "Job done!"

CJ: Why did you become a storyteller?

BZ: Well, I'm not a storyteller in the old sense of the word. I started telling my own stories in poetry, because I was fed up seeing people on television claiming to represent me. It was hot political times. I was living in Aston and Handsworth in Birmingham. There were riots on the street, there was trouble, we were living in a bad situation, bad housing conditions. And every now and then there'd be someone on television and I'd see this line underneath him – community representative – and I'd think, he doesn't represent me. I can speak for myself. And so I started telling my story. And it just happened that a lot of young black people identified with my story, because we were living in the same conditions. And that was my main concern really.

Even before this time I was writing poetry, but I didn't call it poetry. I called it playing with words. In the playground,

I was the guy who could play with words, I could make up rhymes. I would go up to a girl and say, "If I make a poem about you, will you give me a kiss?" And then I'd make up a poem to impress the girl and sometimes I'd get hit! That's how I improved! My mother says that as soon as I started using words I was using them in a very creative, funny way and I would say things that were poetic. I would recognise things that sounded nice and I would just repeat them, because I liked the sound of it.

CJ: Is poetry in the same tradition as other forms of storytelling?

BZ: In West Africa there's a word called "griot". And a griot is a mixture of storyteller, singer-songwriter, poet, comedian, alternative newscaster. If you look at the griot, you cannot help recognising that the western way of looking at art has kind of failed.

In some West African languages, in Arabic, the word for poet and singer and storyteller is the same word. So I think all these divisions, these pigeonholes, it's all about selling the art. What we do is tell stories, and if I need to sing to tell a story I'll sing and if I need to do it in poetry, I'll do it in poetry. If I need to become a character, I'll become a character. If I need to just stand on a soapbox and say, "Look, HIV is a serious thing, let me tell you a story about my brother," so be it. It's the need to communicate something that we find inside us and we use any means necessary.

WHO IS ANANSI THE SPIDER?

Anansi, the god of all stories, is one of the most important characters in West African and Caribbean folklore. Anansi tales are thought to have originated with the Ashanti people in Ghana, for whom the word *anansi* means "spider", and all fables are known as *anansesem* or "spider tales". The stories, which are often about Anansi outwitting more powerful creatures, spread with slavery to the Caribbean and southern United States, where he evolved into "Aunt Nancy". Anansi is a spider who sometimes acts and looks like a man, and is loved for his trickery and cunning and his skill with words. Still popular in oral storytelling traditions, he increasingly appears in books, films, games and songs, and is featured in Marvel comics as "the original spider-man".

Anansi the Spider

ANANSI AND THE BASKET OF STORIES

❝ Once, there were no stories in the world. Anansi the Spider Man decided that he would like to buy some. So he climbed to the top of the very tallest mountain, and shouted up at the sky.

There was a flash of lightning, and an enormous rumble of thunder. It was the voice of Nyame the sky god, who kept all of the stories beside him in a beautiful striped basket.

'Very well, little spider,' chuckled Nyame. 'If you want my stories, you must bring me three things: *Mmboro* the hornets who sting like fire, *Onini* the Python with his many scales, and *Osebo* the leopard with his terrible teeth.'

As he scaled down the mountain Anansi scratched his head with two of his eight legs, thinking carefully.

First he hollowed out a bottle gourd and filled a bowl full of water. Then carefully he tiptoed towards the hornets' nest, wary of their sharp sting. Anansi tipped some of the water over himself and poured the rest over the humming nest. The hornets flew out, buzzing angrily.

'Quick, brothers!' the spider man shouted, 'it's raining! Hide inside my gourd before the rain destroys your wings.'

Spraying water as they went, the hornets thanked Anansi as they zipped past him into the gourd. When the last one was inside Anansi closed the lid with a *thump*!

'One down,' he thought to himself.

Next Anansi picked up the biggest stick he could find and walked into the jungle, muttering to himself.

'Oh yes he is.'

'Oh no he isn't.'

'Oh but he is!'

Suddenly he was disturbed by a slithering, as Onini the python uncoiled himself from behind a rock, his scales scratching on the dry scrub.

'Who are you talking to, little spider?' he hissed.

'I was just having an argument with my wife,' Anansi replied. 'She says that Onini the python is not so long as this stick' – he threw it on the floor – 'but I am not so sure.'

'Foolish spider,' rasped the snake. 'See for yourself!'

With that, the python stretched himself out along-side the stick. 'I am much longer. Look!'

'Hmm,' the tricksy spider scratched his head. 'You are wriggling too much. I can't see. Here, let me tie your tail to the stick to keep still.'

And so he did. 'Now your head is moving too much. Hold on.' And he tied the python's head to the stick until he was bound completely still.

'Now do you see, silly spider?' Onini grunted. But Anansi was already spinning him up in his web to dangle from a tree.

'Two down,' thought the spider man.

A little further along the path Anansi began to dig a large hole. He covered the top with sticks and leaves and hid behind a nearby rock. Soon the heavy footsteps of Osebo the leopard could be felt on the path. Suddenly there was a crash and a howl. Osebo had fallen into the trap.

Looking down into the hole, Anansi shouted down, 'Osebo! Wrap my web around your paws and I will pull you out!' As Osebo did so, Anansi began to run around him in circles, wrapping the sticky web around the leopard's sharp claws and powerful jaws. Caught like a fish in a net, fearsome Osebo was helpless.

At the top of the tallest mountain, Anansi presented his captives to the sky god. There was a rumble of thunder.

'Well done, little spider. I keep my word. You are now the Keeper of Stories, to do with as you please.'

Rubbing his many hands together with glee, Anansi scooped up the beautiful basket of stories and bounded down the mountain. But in his haste he tripped and fell – the striped basket flew from his grasp and broke open. A torrent of words, whispers, shouts and laughter cascaded down the mountain, spilling the stories out into every corner of the world.

'Oh well,' thought Anansi as he picked himself up, 'what is the use of a story if you don't share it?'

And he scuttled back down the mountain to his wife, eager to tell her his story. ❞

Retold for the Story Museum
by storyteller Alex Kanefsky, 2014

Now wype your hands

MORE FAVOURITES

Sometimes there was time to ask our sitters about other favourite characters and stories, or about the one story they would like to leave to future generations. Their answers ranged across the fictional – and non-fictional – universe, but there were many ideas on which they agreed.

DO YOU HAVE ANOTHER FAVOURITE CHARACTER OR STORY?

Malorie Blackman: I love most of the Narnia books: I could be a witch from one of them. Or Agatha Christie's Miss Marple, this little old dear who's got the mind of a bear trap.

Steven Butler: I've made a career out of playing Peter Pan. I also love the books. I would have loved to have been Peter Pan.

Kevin Crossley-Holland: There's a story I heard from my father about two green children who came from another land beneath this earth. It's a medieval story about how we all long to belong. It keeps coming back to me, and I keep going to it as the years pass.

Julia and Malcolm Donaldson: We love a writer called Arnold Lobel, who wrote the *Frog and Toad* books. They're so funny and truthful, and they're kind of fables.

Neil Gaiman: Perhaps something from the Arabian Nights. Or something by James Branch Cabell. Or some of the myths I grew up on, like Thor and Loki. Or the Narnia books. Tolkien's work. And Mary Poppins: P. L. Travers did something very odd in those books, and they're astoundingly powerful.

Jamila Gavin: In Hinduism, the Krishna stories: he's such an amazing character. Out of Hinduism, *Gilgamesh*, one of the most important stories in the whole canon of storytelling. It's extremely ancient but already it's questioning what is life about? Is there an afterlife, and how do we deal with it?

Francis Hardinge: *Alice in Wonderland* springs to mind. I was tempted by the Cheshire Cat. Unfortunately disguising yourself as a smile floating in the air is quite hard!

Charlie Higson: The stories that really had a big impression on me and which stay with me now, and I go back to, are the Greek myths and legends.

Anthony Horowitz: Hannibal Lecter, because I thought it would be enormous fun to lie on a gurney with a leather mask on, terrifying people by my desire to eat human beings; something I don't often mention in interviews, now I think about it. And Dr No, a James Bond villain: please give me metal hands and the high Chinese collar!

Katrice Horsley: There was a wonderful Irish story called "The King of Ireland's Son", a great quest story.

Geraldine McCaughrean: A true discovery to me was *The Epic of Gilgamesh*. It's the oldest written-down story in the history of the world. And it's fresh as the day it was carved with a stick in wet clay. It's a story for everybody who was ever born, about the day you wake up and you realise you are going to die.

Michael Morpurgo: If it hadn't already been occupied by the wretched Philip Pullman, I would have been Long John Silver! Robert Louis Stevenson is the person I want to be, because this man could write. I think his most wonderful book is *Treasure Island*. That was the first book and the first writer that I ever truly fell in love with.

Philip Pullman: An Australian children's classic called *The Magic Pudding*. It is the funniest children's book ever written, with marvellous illustrations by the author, Normal Lindsay.

Katherine Rundell: I loved books which might seem quite placid, like *What Katie Did*, *Anne of Green Gables* and *Ballet Shoes*. They were as comforting as eating bread and butter with hot tea. And there was *Charmed Life* by Diana Wynne-Jones that seemed to me like inhaling sherbet.

Francesca Simon: *The Cat in the Hat*. I love the idea of this character who walks in, completely destroys the house and then just leaves! And I also like his minions Thing One and Thing Two, which is what my husband and I used to call each other when our little child was screaming for us!

Holly Smale: Anne of Green Gables: when I was around twelve I thought she was my kindred spirit.

Clara Vulliamy (and Shirley Hughes): I think we would have made a very good Winnie-the-Pooh and Piglet. I would have been Piglet.

Benjamin Zephaniah: *A Book of Nonsense* by Mervyn Peake, a small book with these very strange characters that live in jars and have really weird names. It was such an inspiration to me.

WHAT STORY WOULD YOU PASS ON TO FUTURE GENERATIONS?

Malorie Blackman: A great big volume of worldwide fairy stories and myths and legends.

Steven Butler: Again, *Peter Pan*.

Ted Dewan: My *Bing Bunny* toddler books: the goal was to bring adults and little people together.

Julia Donaldson: *Watership Down*, a wonderful book.

Neil Gaiman: *The Wind in the Willows*, a glorious little portrait of a time in England that's gone.

Jamila Gavin: Both *Ramayana* and *Gilgamesh* have incredibly important messages.

Frances Hardinge: Again, *Alice in Wonderland*. The eternal message, for both children and adults: don't believe everything you're told, think for yourself. A lot of the time when it seems like the people of authority are talking nonsense, they are talking nonsense.

Charlie Higson: The Greek myths and legends. In the same way as Kew Gardens preserves all the seeds from endangered trees, if you kept the ancient myths and legends from around the world, you'd have the seeds of all literature.

Anthony Horowitz: *The Silver Sword* by Ian Serraillier. It is so important not to forget the sadness, the deprivations, the evil of the Second World War. A fantastically well-written story that echoes down the centuries.

Katrice Horsley: My own story, because if a speech-impaired girl off a rough council estate can become the National Storytelling Laureate, that's a good story!

Shirley Hughes: The Old Testament. It's told in the most amazing way and it's got in it the seeds for *so many* stories. The whole of Renaissance art was telling those stories.

Geraldine McCaughrean: *Gilgamesh*. Something that says live your life from day to day: you're not going to get out of life alive. And yet, you have a child, and there's immortality in your arms.

Michael Morpurgo: A book I wrote called *The Mozart Question*. I would like that to last because it's a strange mix of heaven and hell, and the power of music, which is also the power of stories. Alan Bennett said this wonderful thing, that, as teachers, as grown-ups, as parents, all we are here for, finally, is to pass things on. Some of those old stories are so extraordinary. Aesop's fables. "Hansel and

Gretel". "The Pied Piper of Hamelin". But they need retelling for each generation, otherwise they lose their power and get lost.

Philip Pullman: Of all the children's stories there are, I think the best and the most important is *Alice in Wonderland*. And if I could sneak *Through the Looking Glass* in there as well, I would. Those two books are the fountain from which all other children's literature comes. They're so important, they're so good, they're so funny still. They're so original. There's nothing like them. There was nothing like them before. And if only they were left, I think the whole of children's literature could reconstitute itself from those books alone.

Michael Rosen*:* The story of the fate of my father's uncles. Over the last ten years, I've managed to piece together how both of them ended up on convoys out of France into Auschwitz. They were just a dentist and a clockmaker, just doing stuff in eastern France, then, bit by bit, a kind of net closes around them. Only one year before I was born this was going on. That seems incredible.

Francesca Simon: My favourite book as a child was *Half Magic* by Edward Eager. It's about magic being something unstable that happens to ordinary people. I've always thought that a really profound insight: you think you can be clever with magic, and magic is always more powerful than you are.

Holly Smale: *Winnie-the-Pooh*! It's so funny and so sweet and so warm and full of great messages about friendship and closeness and looking after people.

Clara Vulliamy: Some of the poems by A. A. Milne, like "Disobedience".

Benjamin Zephaniah: I'm going to give you two extremes. The first would be [Alan] Turing, the guy who did so much with computers. It's a very sad story and it's one we should learn from, when people discriminate and bully people. He committed suicide because people found out about his sexuality. And the complete other end of the spectrum, I would like to immortalise the story of Eddie the Eagle! A guy who tried. He didn't look the part. He didn't have the money. He didn't stand a chance. "I'm gonna give it a go!"

Illustrations, from top:
"The Owl and the Pussy-cat", Edward Lear, 1888
Alice's Adventures in Wonderland, *John Tenniel, 1865*
Treasure Island, *Louis Rhead, 1915*
Peter Pan, *Charles Buchel, detail from theatre poster, 1904*

MORE STORIES

Many of the 26 chosen characters went on to appear in or inspire other stories by their original creators and by later generations of writers, film makers, animators and games designers. Here are a few ways in which you can enjoy them further.

MALORIE BLACKMAN
The book in which the Wicked Witch of the West appears
L. Frank Baum, *The Wonderful Wizard of Oz*, G. M. Hill Company, 1900

Other ways to enjoy *The Wonderful Wizard of Oz*
As an audiobook
The Wonderful Wizard of Oz, read by Steve Blane, Dover Books; abridged edition, 2013
The Wonderful Wizard of Oz, read by Bill Nighy, AudioGO Limited; abridged edition, 2013

As a comic
Eric Shanower and Skottie Young, *The Wonderful Wizard of Oz* #1-8, Marvel, 2009

As an app for younger readers
The Wizard Of Oz – An Interactive Children's Story Book HD, by TabTale Ltd, iTunes Store, 2014

As a film
The Wizard of Oz, dir. Victor Fleming, USA, Metro-Goldwyn-Mayer, 1939

Prequels and sequels by L. Frank Baum
The Marvelous Land of Oz, Lond, 1904
Ozma of Oz, Lond, 1907
Dorothy and the Wizard of Oz, Lond, 1908

The Road to Oz, Lond, 1909
The Emerald City of Oz, Lond, 1910
The Patchwork Girl of Oz, Lond, 1913
Tik-Tok of Oz, Lond, 1914
The Scarecrow of Oz, Lond, 1915
Rinkitink in Oz, Lond, 1916
The Lost Princess of Oz, Lond, 1917
The Tin Woodman of Oz, Lond, 1918
The Magic of Oz, Lond, 1919
Glinda of Oz, Lond, 1920

Prequels and sequels by other authors
Ruth Plumly Thompson, *The Royal Book of Oz*, Reilly and Lee, 1921
Gregory Maguire, illustrated by Douglas Smith, *Wicked: The Life and Times of the Wicked Witch of the West*, Regan, 1995. (This novel for adults was later adapted into the hit musical *Wicked*, music and lyrics by Stephen Schwartz and book by Winnie Holzman, 2003.)

STEPHEN BUTLER & FRANCESCA SIMON
The book in which the Queen of Hearts and the Hatter appear
Lewis Carroll, *Alice's Adventures in Wonderland*, Macmillan and Co., 1866

Other ways to enjoy *Alice's Adventures in Wonderland*

As an audiobook

Alice's Adventures in Wonderland, read by David Horovitch, Naxos Audiobooks, 2006

As a comic

Leah Moore and John Reppion, *The Complete Alice in Wonderland,* vols 1–4, Dynamite Entertainment, 2010

As a film

Alice in Wonderland, dir. Tim Burton, Walt Disney Pictures, 2010

Alice in Wonderland, dir. Clyde Geronimi, Wilfred Jackson and Hamilton Luske, Walt Disney Pictures, 1951

Prequels and sequels by Lewis Carroll

Through the Looking Glass and What Alice Found There, Macmillan and Co., 1871

Prequels and sequels by other authors

anon, *Go Ask Alice,* Eyre Methuen Ltd, 1972

Joyce Carol Oates, *Wonderland,* Gollancz, 1972

Robert Gilmore, *Alice in Quantumland,* Sigma Science, 1994

Tad Williams, *Otherland,* four volumes, Orbit: *City of Golden Shadow* (hardback 1996, paperback 1998); *River of Blue Fire* (hardback 1998, paperback 1999); *Mountain of Black Glass* (hardback 1999, paperback 2000); *Sea of Silver Light* (hardback 2001, paperback 2002)

Graphic novel

Bryan Talbot, *Alice in Sunderland,* Jonathan Cape, 2007

Recipes

Heston Blumenthal, *Fantastical Feasts,* Bloomsbury Publishing, 2010

Riddles

Raymond Smullyan, *Alice in Puzzle-Land: A Carrollian Tale for Children Under Eighty,* Penguin, 1984

CRESSIDA COWELL

The book in which Peter Pan appears

J. M. Barrie, *Peter Pan and Wendy,* Hodder and Stoughton, 1911

Other ways to enjoy *Peter Pan*

As an audiobook

Peter Pan, BBC Radio 4 full cast dramatisation, BBC Audiobooks Ltd, 2000

As a film

Peter Pan, dir. Clyde Geronimi, Wilfred Jackson, Hamilton Luske and Jack Kinney, Walt Disney Pictures, 1953

Prequels and sequels by other authors

Dave Barry and Ridley Pearson, *Peter and the Starcatchers,* Hyperion Books, 2004

Dave Barry and Ridley Pearson, *Peter and the Shadow Thieves,* Hyperion Books, 2006

Dave Barry and Ridley Pearson, *Peter and the Secret of Rundoon,* Hyperion Books, 2007

Dave Barry and Ridley Pearson, *Peter and the Sword of Mercy,* Hyperion Books, 2009

Geraldine McCaughrean, *Peter Pan in Scarlet,* Oxford University Press, 2006

Play

Ella Hickson, *Wendy and Peter Pan,* Nick Hern Books (for the RSC), 2013

Film

Hook, dir. Steven Spielberg, Tri-Star Pictures, 1991

Peter Pan 2: Return to Never Land, dir. Robin Budd, Donavan Cook, Walt Disney Pictures, 2002

KEVIN CROSSLEY-HOLLAND

The book in which Merlin first appears

Geoffrey of Monmouth, *The History of the Kings of Britain,* translated by Lewis Thorpe, Penguin Classics, 1973

Other ways to enjoy the legends of King Arthur and the Knights of the Round Table, in which Merlin is an important character

As a book

Kevin Crossley-Holland, *Arthur and the Seeing Stone,* Orion, 2000

Geraldine McCaughrean, *King Arthur and a world of other stories,* Orion, 2011

For younger readers:

Marcia Williams, *King Arthur and the Knights of the Round Table,* Walker, 2010

As a comic

Meg Cabot, *Avalon High,* Macmillan, 2006

As a film

The Sword in the Stone, dir. Wolfgang Reitherman, Walt Disney Pictures, 1963

As a TV series

Merlin, dir. Jeremy Webb, Alice Troughton, David Moore, Justin Molotnikov, Ashley Way, Ed Fraiman, James Hawes, Metin Hüseyin, Alex Pillai, Stuart Orme and Declan O'Dwyer, BBC, 2008–2012

TED & PANDORA DEWAN

The book in which Pod and Arrietty appear

Mary Norton, *The Borrowers,* Dent, 1952

Other ways to enjoy *The Borrowers*

As an audiobook

The Borrowers, read by Samantha Bond, Puffin Audio Books, 2003

As a TV adaptation
The Borrowers, dir. Tom Harper, Universal Pictures, 2012
The Borrowers (Series 1 and 2), dir. Ian Holm, BBC
Classics, 2011

Prequels and sequels by Mary Norton
The Borrowers Afield, J. M. Dent and Sons, 1955
The Borrowers Afloat, J. M. Dent and Sons, 1959
The Borrowers Aloft, J. M. Dent and Sons, 1961
Poor Stainless: A New Story About the Borrowers, J. M. Dent
and Sons, 1971
The Borrowers Avenged, Kestrel Books, 1982

Film
Arrietty, dir. Hiromasa Yonebayashi, Studio Ghibli, 2010

JULIA & MALCOLM DONALDSON
**The book in which the Owl and the Pussycat
appear**
Edward Lear, *Nonsense Songs, Botany and Alphabets,* Robert
John Bush, 1871

Prequels and sequels by Edward Lear
A Book of Nonsense, Thomas McLean, 1846

Prequels and sequels by other authors
Julia Donaldson, illustrated by Charlotte Voake, *The Further
Adventures of the Owl and the Pussy-cat*, Puffin, 2013
Eric Idle, *The Quite Remarkable Adventures of the Owl and
the Pussycat*, Dove Books, 1996
Beatrix Potter, *The Tale of Little Pig Robinson*, Frederick
Warne & Co., 1930

Play
Sheila Ruskin and David Wood, *The Owl and the Pussycat
Went to See*, Samuel French, 1970

NEIL GAIMAN
The book in which Badger appears
Kenneth Grahame, *The Wind in the Willows,* Methuen and
Co., 1908

Other ways to enjoy *The Wind in the Willows*
As an audiobook
The Wind in the Willows, read by Alan Bennett, BBC, 2006

As a radio play
Alan Bennett, *The Wind in the Willows*, BBC, 1994

As a film
The Wind in the Willows, dir. Mark Hall, Thames Television,
1983
The Wind in the Willows, dir. Dave Unwin, Carlton UK,
1995
The Wind in the Willows, dir. Terry Jones, Columbia
Pictures, 1996
The Wind in the Willows, dir. Rachel Talahay, BBC, 2006

As a play
A. A. Milne, *Toad of Toad Hall,* Methuen, 1929
Alan Bennett, *The Wind in the Willows*, Faber and Faber,
1991

Prequels and sequels by other authors
William Horwood, *The Willows in Winter*, Harper Collins,
1993
William Horwood, *Toad Triumphant*, Harper Collins, 1995
William Horwood, *The Willows and Beyond*, Harper
Collins, 1996
William Horwood, *The Willows at Christmas*, Harper
Collins, 1999
Jan Needle, *Wild Wood*, Deutsch, 1981
Dixon Scott, *A Fresh Wind in the Willows*, Heinemann,
1983

JAMILA GAVIN
The book in which Hanuman appears
Valmiki, *The Ramayana,* translated by Ashia Sattar,
Penguin, 2000

Other ways to enjoy stories about Hanuman
In books
Milo Beach, *Adventures of Rama: with Illustrations from
a Sixteenth-Century Mughal Manuscript*, Grantha
Corporation, 2011
Jamila Gavin, *Tales from India*, Templar, 2011
J. E. P. Gray, *Oxford Tales from India*, Oxford University
Press, 2001

Prequels and sequels by other authors
anon., *The Mahabarata*, translated by John D. Smith,
Penguin, 2009
Jamila Gavin, *Monkey in the Stars*, Mammoth, 1998

FRANCES HARDINGE
The book in which the Scarlet Pimpernel appears
Baroness Emma Orzcy, *The Scarlet Pimpernel,* Lond, 1905

Other ways to enjoy *The Scarlet Pimpernel*
As a play
Baroness Emma Orzcy, *The Scarlet Pimpernel,* Lond, 1903

As a TV adaptation
The Scarlet Pimpernel, dir. Edward Bennett, Patrick Lau,
Simon Langton and Graham Theakston, A&E Television
Networks, 2000

As a film
The Scarlet Pimpernel, dir. Harold Young, London Film
Productions, 1934
The Scarlet Pimpernel, dir. Clive Donner, Acorn Media,
1982

Prequels and sequels by Baroness Orczy
I Will Repay, Eveleigh Nash and Grayson, 1906

The Elusive Pimpernel, Hutchinson, 1908
El Dorado, Hodder and Stoughton, 1913
Lord Tony's Wife, Lond, 1917
The Triumph of the Scarlet Pimpernel, Hodder and Stoughton, 1922
Sir Percy Hits Back, Hodder and Stoughton, 1927
The Way of the Scarlet Pimpernel, Hodder and Stoughton, 1933
Sir Percy Leads the Band, Hodder and Stoughton, 1936
Mam'zelle Guillotine, Hodder and Stoughton, 1940

Prequels and sequels by other authors

Geoffrey Trease, *Thunder of Valmy,* Macmillan, 1960

Graphic novel

Alan Moore, *The League of Extraordinary Gentlemen,* America's Best Comics, 2000

TV

Doctor Who: The Reign of Terror, dir. John Gorrie and Henric Hirsch, BBC, 1964

Film

The Scarlet Pumpernickel, dir. Charles M. Jones, Warner Bros, 1950 (a Daffy Duck cartoon)

CHARLIE HIGSON

The books in which Boromir appears

J. R. R. Tolkien, *The Fellowship of the Ring* and *The Two Towers* (volumes I and II of the *Lord of the Rings* trilogy), Collins, 1954 & 1955

Other ways to enjoy *The Lord of the Rings*

As an audio book
The Fellowship of the Ring, read by Rob Inglis, Harper Collins, 2007

As a film
The Lord of the Rings: The Fellowship of the Ring, dir. Peter Jackson, New Line Cinema, 2001

As a game
The Lord of the Rings: The Card Game, Fantasy Flight Games, 2011
Lord of the Rings, Warhammer, Games Workshop, 2001

Prequels and sequels by J. R. R. Tolkien

The Hobbit, George, Allen and Unwin, 1937
Return of the King, Collins, 1956
The Silmarillion, Allen & Unwin, 1977

Film

The Lord of the Rings: The Fellowship of the Ring, dir. Peter Jackson, New Line Cinema, 2001
The Lord of the Rings: The Two Towers, dir. Peter Jackson, New Line Cinema, 2002
The Lord of the Rings: Return of the King, dir. Peter Jackson, New Line Cinema, 2003
The Hunt for Gollum, dir. Chris Bouchard, Independent Online Cinema, 2009

SHIRLEY HUGHES & CLARA VULLIAMY

The play in which Lady Bracknell and Miss Prism appear

Oscar Wilde, *The Importance of Being Earnest,* Leonard Smithers and Co., 1899

Other ways to enjoy *The Importance of Being Earnest*

As a radio adaptation
The Importance of Being Earnest, BBC Radio 3 full cast production, BBC Audiobooks Ltd, 2001

As a film
The Importance of Being Earnest, dir. Anthony Asquith, British Film Makers, 1952
The Importance of Being Earnest, dir. Oliver Parker, Miramax, 2002

Prequels and sequels

Play
Robert Johnson, *In a Handbag Darkly,* Broken Home Theatre Company, 2009

ANTONY HOROWITZ

The book in which Dr Jekyll and Mr Hyde appear

Robert Louis Stevenson, *Strange Case of Dr Jekyll and Mr Hyde,* Longman Green & Co, 1866

Other ways to enjoy *Dr Jekyll and Mr Hyde*

As a book (for younger readers)
Rob Lloyd Jones, *Dr Jekyll & Mr Hyde* (Young Reading, Series 3), Usborne, 2010

As a film
Dr Jekyll and Mr Hyde, dir. Rouben Mamoulian, Paramount Pictures, 1931

Prequels and sequels by other authors

Loren D. Estleman, *Dr Jekyll and Mr Holmes,* Titan, 2010
Valerie Martin, *Mary Reilly,* Doubleday, 1990

TV

Jekyll, dir. Matt Lipsey and Douglas Mackinnon, BBC, 2007
For younger viewers:
Julia Jekyll and Harriet Hyde, dir. Jeremy Swan, BBC, 1995–1998

Film

Igor, Anthony Leondis, Exodus Film Group, 2008
The League of Extraordinary Gentlemen, dir. Stephen Norrington, Twentieth Century Fox, 2003
Van Helsing, dir. Stephen Sommers, Universal Pictures, 2004

KATRICE HORSLEY
The book in which Mary Poppins appears
P. L. Travers, *Mary Poppins*, G. Howe, 1934

Other ways to enjoy *Mary Poppins*
As a film
Mary Poppins, dir. Robert Stevenson, Walt Disney Productions, 1964

Prequels and sequels by P. L. Travers
Mary Poppins Comes Back, Dickson & Thompson, 1935
Mary Poppins Opens the Door, P. Davies, 1943
Mary Poppins in the Park, P. Davies, 1952
Mary Poppins From A to Z, Collins, 1965
Mary Poppins in the Kitchen, Collins, 1977
Mary Poppins in Cherry Tree Lane, Collins, 1982
Mary Poppins and the House Next Door, Collins, 1988

TERRY JONES
The book in which Rupert Bear appears
Alfred Bestall, "Rupert and King Frost", *Rupert's Adventure Book*, Daily Express Publications, 1940

Other ways to enjoy Rupert Bear
In a newspaper
The comic strip is still published daily in the *Daily Express*

In an annual
From 1936 onwards, a new Rupert annual has been published every year. The Followers of Rupert hold a complete listing for all the annuals:
www.rupertbear.co.uk/rupert-annuals_PC5
(5 January 2014). The most recent edition is *The Rupert Annual 2014*, No. 78, Egmont, 2013

TV
The Adventures of Rupert, dir. Ale Scott, Freemantle Home Entertainment, 2010

GERALDINE McCAUGHREAN
The book in which Bellerophon appears
Homer, *The Iliad*, Everyman's Library, 1969

Other ways to enjoy stories about Bellerophon
As a graphic novel for younger readers
Marcia Williams, *Greek Myths*, Walker Books, 2006

As a book
Robert Graves, *The Greek Myths: The Complete and Definitive Edition*, Penguin, 2011
Marianna Meyer, *Pegasus*, William Morrow, 1998

Prequels and sequels by other authors
John Barth, *Chimera,* Deutsch, 1974

Film
Clash of the Titans, dir. Desmond Davies, Metro-Goldwyn-Mayer, 1981

MICHAEL MORPURGO
The book in which Magwitch appears
Charles Dickens, *Great Expectations*, Chapman and Hall, 1860–61

Other ways to enjoy *Great Expectations*
As an audiobook
Great Expectations, read by Martin Jarvis, Fantom Films Limited, 2012

As a comic
Jen Green, *Great Expectations*, Classical Comics, 2009

As a film
Great Expectations, dir. David Lean, Universal Studios, 1946
Great Expectations, dir. Joseph Hardy, Transcontinental Films, 1974
Great Expectations, dir. Mike Newell, Lionsgate, 2012

TV
Great Expectations, dir. Brian Kirk, BBC, 2011

Prequels and sequels by other authors
Ronald Frame, *Havisham*, Faber & Faber, 2013

TERRY PRATCHETT
The book in which William appears
Richmal Crompton, *Just William*, George Newnes, 1922

Other ways to enjoy *Just William*
As an audiobook
The BBC Radio series read by Martin Jarvis in the 1990s is one of the best-known and most popular adaptations. The BBC has released 21 collections of the readings, including some live recitals and special compilations. A complete list can be found at:
wikipedia.org/wiki/Just_William_(BBC_Radio_series)

As a film
Just William's Luck, dir. Val Guest, Diadem Films, 1950

TV adaptation
Just William, dir. David Giles, Talisman Films, 1994
Just William, dir. Paul Seed, BBC, 2010

Prequels and sequels
Richmal Crompton wrote 39 "Just William" books: all are collections of short stories except for one novel, *Just William's Luck*.

PHILIP PULLMAN
The book in which Long John Silver appears
Robert Louis Stevenson, *Treasure Island*, Cassell & Co., 1883

Other ways to enjoy *Treasure Island*
As an audiobook
Treasure Island, read by Jasper Britton (unabridged), Naxos Junior Classics, 2007

As a comic
Marvel Illustrated: Treasure Island, Marvel, 2007

As a film
Treasure Island, dir. Byron Haskins, Walt Disney Pictures, 1950
Treasure Island, dir. Fraser Clarke Heston, Turner Network Television, 1990
Muppet Treasure Island, dir. Brian Henson, Walt Disney Pictures, 1996
Treasure Planet, dir. Ron Clements, Walt Disney Pictures, 2002

The influence of *Treasure Island* can clearly be seen in many adventure films about pirates, from *Captain Blood* (1935) to the *Pirates of the Caribbean* series (2003–).

Prequels and sequels by other authors
Ronald Delderfield, *The Adventures of Ben Gunn*, Hodder and Stoughton, 1972
Andrew Motion, *Silver: Return to Treasure Island*, Jonathan Cape, 2012

MICHAEL ROSEN
The book in which Till Eulenspiegel appears
Johannes Grüninger, *Einkurtzweilig Lesen von Dyl Ulenspiegel, geborenuß dem Land zu Brunßwick, wieerseinlebenvolbracht hat*, 1510–12

Other ways to enjoy Till Eulenspiegel
As a film
Jester Till (German with English subtitles), dir. Eberhard Junkersdorf, Munich Animation Film, 2003

Prequels and sequels by other authors
Michael Rosen, *Till Owlyglass*, Walker Books, 1990, reissued 2014

KATHERINE RUNDELL
The book in which the Wild Thing appears
Maurice Sendak, *Where the Wild Things Are*, Bodley Head, 1967

Other ways to enjoy Where the Wild Things Are
As a film
Where the Wild Things Are and Other Maurice Sendak Stories (Scholastic Video Collection), music and narration by Peter Schickele, New Video Group, 1973
Where the Wild Things Are, dir. Spike Jonze, Warner Bros, 2009

As an opera
Where the Wild Things Are: a fantasy opera, composer Oliver Knussen, 1983. Available on CD released by Arabesque in 1999, and as a Glyndebourne performance on DVD released by NVC Arts/Warner Classics in 2010

HOLLY SMALE
The book in which the White Witch appears
C. S. Lewis, *The Lion, the Witch and the Wardrobe*, Geoffrey Blessing, 1950

Other ways to enjoy *The Lion, the Witch and the Wardrobe*
As an audiobook
The Lion, the Witch and the Wardrobe, read by Michael York, Harper Collins Audiobooks, 2000
The Lion, the Witch and the Wardrobe, read by Jim Broadbent, Harper Collins Audiobooks, 2005

As a film
The Lion, the Witch and the Wardrobe, dir. Andrew Adamson, Walt Disney Pictures, 2005

As a TV series
The Lion, the Witch and the Wardrobe, dir. Marilyn Fox, BBC, 1988

Prequels and sequels by C. S. Lewis
Prince Caspian: The Return to Narnia, Geoffrey Blessing, 1951
The Voyage of the Dawn Treader, Geoffrey Blessing, 1952
The Silver Chair, Geoffrey Blessing, 1953
The Horse and His Boy, Geoffrey Blessing, 1954
The Magician's Nephew, Bodley Head, 1955
The Last Battle, Bodley Head, 1956

BENJAMIN ZEPHANIAH
Books in which traditional Anansi stories appear
Vera Aardema, *Anansi Finds a Fool: An Ashanti Tale*, Dial Books, 1992
Peggy Appiah, *The Pineapple Child and Other Tales from the Ashanti*, Andre Deutsch, 1969
Gerald McDermott, *Anansi the Spider: A Tale from the Ashanti*, Holt Rinehart and Winston, 1972

Other appearances and reimaginings
C. B. Cebulski, *Spider-Man: Fairy Tales #2*, Marvel, 2007
Neil Gaiman, *American Gods*, Headline, 2001
Neil Gaiman, *Anansi Boys*, Headline, 2005
China Miéville, *King Rat*, Saint Martin's Press, 1998

The Brer Rabbit stories of North America are thought to have developed from the Anansi stories, supposedly when Native American and Caribbean traditions combined during the time of slavery.

Full-length versions of the author interviews and their original stories, as well as readings from some of the chosen stories, are freely available on the Story Museum website: www.storymuseum.org.uk/26Characters

thestory museum

WHY DOES THE WORLD NEED A STORY MUSEUM?

We ended each conversation by asking the authors why stories matter, whether stories need museums and what a story museum should do. Their answers embraced the many different roles stories play in our lives and the many ways in which dedicated story museums – existing and imagined – can help us understand and enjoy them. We took careful notes.

Malorie Blackman: I think the world definitely needs a story museum. Stories are a way that we understand not just the world but ourselves. It is important for children to be exposed to stories from this country and around the world, because there's such a rich storytelling tradition in all cultures, be it oral or literary. We need somewhere we can look at that and analyse that and think, "What purpose does this story serve and why do I like it?"

It's also about teaching empathy, being able to see the world through other people's eyes. You open a book, and it's like opening a door into new thoughts, new ideas, new feelings, new people, new worlds. That's what makes them so special. So I think it's *really* important we have somewhere we can reflect on that.

Steven Butler: It keeps stories alive! I was a child of the Roald Dahl generation and it shocks me when people don't know those books. A museum of story keeps a story timeless, which is brilliant.

Cressida Cowell: It gets children thinking about the way that stories are written. Hopefully it gets them thinking that this is something that some of them can do. At school, even though I spent my life writing stories, I didn't realise it was a career I could do. There are a lot of jobs that involve storytelling. And creativity – whatever you do – is immensely important. I would *really* love to see more importance being placed on a creative element in the national curriculum, and GCSE, and A-level, and more emphasis on creative writing beyond primary level.

We've got Seven Stories in Newcastle, and the Story Museum coming, and I think it's really important to celebrate that we have some of the best storytellers in the world. It's something that we should be really proud of in Britain.

Kevin Crossley-Holland: Stories are our daily bread. They are the way we prove how human we are and empathise with other human beings: we feel their fears, their hopes, their longings. Stories are always, but always, about how much the same we are, how different we are, but how in any case you and I are the story. And there is no story museum in the world.

To my mind a story museum is a storehouse, or a quarry, or a hoard, of the world's greatest stories. It's a place where we find out the who and what and why and when and where and how of story. Story is how we look forward, and it's how we look back. And we need to look back because stories get forgotten rather more quickly than people imagine. It's crucial that we celebrate them, reinvent them, retell them and make new ones.

Ted Dewan: When you go through the doors, just as when you open the cover of a book, you'll be encouraged to suspend disbelief. The thing you do to enter the world of a story, which is a trick of imagination, will happen. It won't just be a children's museum, because stories are for all of us. And each time you visit, like each time you visit a good story, it becomes deeper. How do you exhibit a story? Well, maybe there's something about what stories are for that a museum can bring to the fore.

Julia Donaldson: The world has of course already got one brilliant museum of children's books in Newcastle, Seven Stories. It's got a really good bookshop, it has exhibitions, it's got a storytelling floor. I think if the one in Oxford can do all of that, it's such an opportunity for children and parents to find out about writers and illustrators of the past. We all need stories in our lives and it's interesting to find out the background to some of those stories.

Neil Gaiman: There are lots of things that are vital to being human. Things like food, culture, warmth. The things that are most vital, and most easy to overlook, are stories. Because we're surrounded by them, we can take them for granted.

My cousin Helen is 94. She, as a young woman, was in the Warsaw ghetto. Possession of a book meant an automatic death sentence, without trial. The Germans would put a gun to your head and press the trigger. Helen got hold of a copy of *Gone with the Wind*. And every night she would read another two or three chapters by candlelight, with the windows carefully blocked so nobody could see light getting out. And then she'd hide that copy in a space in the wall.

When the sewing circle were ordered to sew clothes for soldiers, they'd sit and they'd sew and she'd tell them the story of what she'd read in *Gone with the Wind* the night before. They could all have been killed, but it was important enough to them to have a story, to care about what happened to people who hadn't existed, except in the mind of Margaret Mitchell, that they risked death. People that think stories aren't important – aren't as important as breathing, aren't as important as warmth, aren't as important as life – are missing the point. And that's why I think there should be a story museum.

Jamila Gavin: I would really like to think that the art of storytelling could be perpetuated. I've met many teachers who have lost the ability. I'd like to think that teachers might come and learn how to tell stories to their children. I think children are pretty good at telling stories and they lose it. Which is another whole story about what we're doing in education. But I think storytelling is essential.

Frances Hardinge: Museums are the way we celebrate the things that we consider important. Stories are important. Stories are the way we recognise and understand the world and ourselves. They're an entertaining and essential mirror.

Charlie Higson: I think that anything that preserves stories, that encourages stories, that will lead children to find stories that they might not otherwise stumble across is great. And to have a centre where people can tell stories, the very earliest form of storytelling, and writers will enjoy going to, is a great thing. Stories will survive whatever happens, but anything that gives them a home has got to be good.

Anthony Horowitz: Does the world need a story museum? Well, "need" is a funny word, isn't it? Need is about pragmatism and about mechanics, about survival. I'm not sure really "need" is the right word. I think the world will benefit from a story museum, mainly because young people don't just want to read books. They want to devour the books, they want to enter the books, they want to go behind the books, they want to discover the world of the books: the authors, the illustrators, the history, the associated facts and figures, everything. And to be able to walk into a wonderful building in the middle of Oxford and live, breathe, see, be part of story, is a fantastic experience. So, "need", no. But enjoy, definitely.

Katrice Horsley: The Story Museum is fantastic. What is wonderful is that it is totally inclusive. Stories are not just about words on a page. I love books. I adore books. But for me, they are almost fossils of stories. And you can only chip away at them if you have the code. So if you are not literate in the language the book is written in, you can't access the story.

For me stories are not just visual things, they are totally sensory things. I want to immerse myself in the thick pelt, the thick syrup of story. I want to taste story, hear story, see story, feel story. That is what the Story Museum does. Irrespective of whether you can read or write, the Story Museum will saturate all of your story senses.

Shirley Hughes: You could go on for ever about how it's absolutely crucial. It's terribly important. It's increasingly important. I grew up in an era of total boredom; there was *nothing* to do. The radio was all we had in World War Two. So out of boredom I drew, just to liven things up. Now I think children are almost *over*-entertained, and if storytelling isn't absolutely *central* to their early upbringing, then it's just crowded out. It's a human thing: you hold the child on your lap and read the story book to them or tell them a story. It goes back way beyond literacy, but I think it's important for it to be central. We need it, don't we?

Terry Jones: I think it's a good idea to have a story museum because stories are a vital part of our everyday life. They teach us about the world, and I think as children that's what we learn through stories. They're vital things.

Geraldine McCaughrean: I hope it will be a haven, like a wildlife park, where stories can live in their natural state. Without anybody saying, "Study this, analyse this, have an opinion about this, go away and write a story in your best handwriting that is a version of this." Just come and roll around in new-mown hay, in that *stuff* of story, and see what it does to you. Because story acts on people in different ways. Some get a direct pleasure from the sound of stories, the mellifluous language. Some are entirely visual, so while they're listening to a story they're seeing pictures. And some just feel it: they're identifying with the people in the story, and becoming someone else, escaping their own limitations.

Story doesn't have a motive. Story is just there. We're

born seeking it, which is very odd. I don't understand why the human race should be born seeking story. I think it comes from the fact that babies are born asking "Why?" The first thing a child says is "Why?" All the time we're trying to work out how the world works.

Michael Morpurgo: The world needs stories more than it's ever needed stories. I'll give you just one example of one story and why we need it. And it follows on from that, why we need a story museum. Hans Christian Andersen wrote a story called *The Emperor's New Clothes*, which we know. Well, we think we know, but we probably haven't read it for a long time. It's the kind of story that should be like a bible for all of us, but particularly for those in power, and aspiring to power. It tells us so much about who we are and the pretensions we have, and the disguises, and the hypocrisies. Aesop's fables do the same thing. These elemental stories, which purport to be about emperors and foxes and crows, which are of course about us and our frailties, teach us so much about ourselves.

Why have a museum? Because it seems to me that without stories, and without an understanding of stories, we don't understand ourselves, we don't understand the world about us. And we don't understand the relations between ourselves and those people around us. Because what stories give us is an insight into ourselves, a huge insight into other people, other cultures, other places. So it's a gathering of all the knowledge and understanding that we need. For me that's probably the most important kind of museum that you can have, providing you can also hear the stories and see the pictures, that it is presented in a way which is lively and imaginative, which is I'm sure what they're going to do.

Terry Pratchett: I find that very difficult. It's like saying, why do human beings need to breathe? It's like asking a fish exactly what water is for.

I would point back to the stories that my mother told me. I remember, when she took me to school, which was quite a long way on foot, she would tell me things. She told me a lot of the Greek myths. I think people who don't talk to their kids do them a great disservice.

Philip Pullman: It's a wonderful idea to have a story museum, because it shows we (we the human race, not just we the people of Oxford) are paying proper attention to stories. Stories are the way we think. We think in stories, we think through stories, we think about ourselves in terms of a story. And the more we understand stories and think about them and study them, the more I think we'll know about ourselves as human beings. Besides, they're such fun.

Michael Rosen: What's special about a museum of stories is that it can do lots of different things in different ways, all at the same time. If you think about the great museums – the British Museum, the Louvre, the Science Museum, the Natural History Museum – these are places that you can't do all in a day. The best way is to go often, and you start building your own set of stories, your own ways into understanding things.

I would love to think that you'd come back over and over again. Sometimes you would get a live storytelling, the simplest, most basic face-to-face thing that we do with that kind of a story. Another time you might see some kind of animation or comic strip or narrative art or even, maybe, forms of sculpture, and you're going to be interacting with that and thinking, "Oh, look, story doesn't need words!" Another time, you might recognise a scene from *Alice in Wonderland* or *The Hobbit*. These moments have great power and a museum could capture many moments. Maybe you could come, as a class of children, and improvise around stories, get into a story, and take on the roles. There are so many hundreds of ways to get into it and no one has ever done it like that. I would love this place to have a sense that the world is full of many different kinds of stories.

Katherine Rundell: Perhaps the most extraordinary thing about the Story Museum is that it has gathered together the most gorgeous gems of the literature that we've accumulated and laid them out for children to see. It seems to me the most extraordinary archive of the things that matter most to children. I can't imagine childhood without stories. This is a thing that has been lacking from the world.

Francesca Simon: We live in such a utilitarian age where there's this idea that if you input that data, you'll get that result. Give children that to study, and they'll get this result! Stories break free from that. I have never met a child who didn't love being read to, hearing a story. You can do something to destroy that, but I think it's hardwired into everyone to love stories, love storytelling, love being part of a story. It's an incredible activity and it's one of those things that people don't do that much any more, actually listen to stories together, sit and read together. It's incredibly precious.

Britain is so brilliant at storytelling. The legacy of children's writers from this country is astounding. To have something that reminds people of that amazing heritage, to really celebrate that, away from school and exams, I think is so important.

I am a really academic person, but my reading was completely separate from school. It's vital that children be allowed to read what they want to read! That's why libraries are so important. You give a child a library card, they can wander in the library and they can check ten books out. They can check ten stupid books. They can check out anything! It doesn't matter. And every week ten more, ten more, ten more. It's this big treasure trove. I used to read alphabetically just to see what I would uncover, regardless of what the book was, of what the subject was. It was exciting. The Story Museum is a living library.

Holly Smale: Stories are one of the things that separate us from dogs and cats and it's great to be able to celebrate that and appreciate it properly. You could see a library as being a portal where the books themselves are the doors. A story museum celebrates the worlds inside those doors and shows you what's inside. It's magical going into a library, because you know in your head how many worlds there are within, but a museum actually demonstrates that.

Clara Vulliamy: Children need stories like they need vitamin C. The Story Museum is going to be such a wealth of treasures, such a treat for children to visit, and it's also very exciting to think, of all the hundreds of thousands of children who are going to come through that door, among them will be the next generation of storytellers, of writers, illustrators, playwrights, poets. That's the most exciting thing of all.

Benjamin Zephaniah: Personally, I worry that our stories will die out, be forgotten. Fortunately at the moment there's a boom in children's literature and storytelling generally, but you just never know what the future is, so *now* is the time to do it. Our stories are really important. And when I talk about our stories I don't just mean the stories of Benjamin Zephaniah, or the rich and the famous, or the great stories that we know from our childhood — be that *Alice in Wonderland* or whatever it is — but the stories of everyday people.

To me stories have many functions, but the main two are probably to record our history, in a really basic grassroots way; and to give us hope, because if you are finding it very difficult getting on and doing something in life, there is nothing like looking back and seeing that there was a strange guy long ago called Cambridge that did it! So if he can do it, I can do it. I think all our stories are important, even what some could see superficially as stories of failure and things that didn't work, because we learn from them.

The Story Museum celebrates stories in all forms and explores their enduring power to teach and delight. Founded in 2003, it began by taking stories and storytellers into schools and communities. Since 2009 it has gradually been transforming a large, dilapidated building in the centre of Oxford into an unusual museum, with the help of authors, artists, teachers, other cultural organisations and volunteers of all ages. It is one of a growing array of venues that present different aspects of our story heritage or encourage people to create stories of their own. For further information, visit www.storymuseum.org.uk

ACKNOWLEDGEMENTS

26 Characters was a happy collaboration between many talented and generous people. But it would not have been possible without the inspiration, encouragement and practical support of Ginny Battcock, who planted the original seed and nurtured it through to fruition.

Costumes and props: Coordinated by Ginny Battcock. With thanks to Maura Allen, Ally Baker, Tish Francis and Sally Yeomans; Malgosia Nowak-Kemp of Oxford University Museum of Natural History; Lucy Barrett, Froo Gager, Katie Price, Ann Taylor, Joseph Taylor and Harriet Wilcox of the Royal Shakespeare Company costume department; and Liz Murray of the National Theatre costume department.

Make-up: Sue Parsons, Sophie Everett, Melanie Winning and Lynn Fraser.

Research, writing, text and picture editing, and copyright clearances: Natalie Balchin, Katie Battcock, Michael Battcock, Isobel Booth, Jane Cockcroft, Alex Coke, Matthew Davies, Honor Dawkins-Stean, Tom Donegan, Sophie Hutcheon, Rhiannon Jones, Hannah Malyon, Eka Morgan, Kim Pickin, Duncan Saunders, Kate Sayer, Hannah Smith, Sophie Smith and Hennie Thomson. Without whom Alice Rochester would not exist.

Original stories and illustrations: Neill Cameron, Robert Fresson, Jamila Gavin, Alex Kanefsky and Geraldine McCaughrean.

Design and editing: Amanda Brookes and Paul Forty of Brookes Forty.

26 Characters logo: One.

The Story Museum would also like to thank: the participating authors, their assistants, agents, publishers and families; the Jones family – Ondine, Amber, Sasha and of course Cambridge; our staff, interns, freelances and volunteers, patrons and trustee board for their advice and encouragement; and our generous funders and sponsors, especially Arts Council England, the Garfield Weston Foundation, Humphrey and Ginny Battcock, Will Bowen and One.

COPYRIGHT PERMISSIONS

Malorie Blackman: quotation on p. 12 & extract on p. 15 from chapters 11 & 12 of *The Wonderful Wizard of Oz* by L. Frank Baum, Chicago, G. M. Hill Company, 1900; illustration on p.14 and book cover on p. 15 by W. W. Denslow, *The Wonderful Wizard of Oz*, G. M. Hill Company, 1900.

Steven Butler & Francesca Simon: quotations on p. 16 from chapters 7 & 8 and extract on p. 21 from chapter 11 of *Alice's Adventures in Wonderland* by Lewis Carroll, London, Macmillan & Co., 1865; illustrations on pp. 20 & 21 and book cover on p. 21 by John Tenniel, *Alice's Adventures in Wonderland*, Macmillan & Co, 1865.

Cressida Cowell: quotation on p. 22 and extract on p. 25 from chapters 15 & 3 of *Peter and Wendy* by J. M. Barrie, London, Hodder & Stoughton, 1911; illustration on p. 25 by Gwynned, M. Hudson, *Peter Pan and Wendy*, Hodder & Stoughton, 1931, reprinted with kind permission of Great Ormond Street Hospital Children's Charity. Illustration on p. 24 © Cressida Cowell, 2014.

Kevin Crossley-Holland: quotation on p. 26 and extract on p. 29 from *The Red Dragon and White Dragon*, adapted from *The Seeing Stone*, 2000, Orion Publishing Group © Kevin Crossley-Holland, 2014. Illustration on p. 28, Mary Evans Picture Library/Alamy.

Ted & Pandora Dewan: quotation on p. 30 and extract on p. 33 from chapters 5 & 4 of *The Borrowers* by Mary Norton, London, Orion Publishing Group, 2011, text copyright © Mary Norton, 1955; book cover on p. 32 and illustration on p. 33, *The Borrowers*, London, Orion Publishing Group, 2011, illustrations copyright © Diana Stanley 1952.

Julia & Malcolm Donaldson: quotation on p. 34 and extract on p. 37 from "The Owl and the Pussy-cat" by Edward Lear, in *Songs, Stories, Botany and Alphabets,* London, Robert John Bush, 1871; book cover on p. 37, Edward Lear, *Nonsense Songs and Stories*, London and New York, Frederick Warne and Co, 1888.

Neil Gaiman: quotation on p. 38 and extract on p. 41 from chapter 4 of *The Wind in the Willows* by Kenneth Grahame, London, Methuen & Co. Ltd, 1908; illustration on p. 41 by E. H. Shepard in *The Wind in the Willows*, 1908, copyright © The Shepard Trust, reproduced with permission of Curtis Brown Ltd, London, reprinted by permission of Egmont Publishing.

Jamila Gavin: quotation on p. 42 and extract on pp. 46–7 from *How Hanuman Found Sita* © Jamila Gavin, 2014; illustration on p. 45: Dinodia Photos/Alamy.

Frances Hardinge: quotation on p. 48 and extract on p. 51 from chapters 4 & 1 of *The Scarlet Pimpernel* by Baroness Orczy, London, Greening, 1905; both reprinted by permission of A. P. Watt at United Agents on behalf of Sara Orczy-Barstow Brown. Illustration on p. 50 © Francis Hardinge, 2014.

Charlie Higson: quotation on p. 52 and extract on p. 55 from chapters 2 & 10 of *The Fellowship of the Ring* by J. R. R. Tolkien, London, George Allen and Unwin, 1954, both reprinted by permission of HarperCollins Publishers Ltd, *The Fellowship of the Ring* © Fourth Age Limited 1954, 1955, 1966; book cover on p. 55 reprinted by permission of HarperCollins Publishers Ltd,

© (1970) (J.R.R Tolkien); photograph on p. 54 © The Story Museum, 2014. We wish to thank the Tolkien Estate for permitting photographic representation of Charlie Higson as Boromir.

Anthony Horowitz: quotation on p. 56 and extract on p. 59 from chapters 9 & 1 of *Strange Case of Dr Jekyll and Mr Hyde* by Robert Louis Stevenson, London, Longmans, 1886; illustration on p. 59, Image Asset Management Ltd/Alamy.

Katrice Horsley: quotation on p. 60 and extract on p. 63 from chapter 1 of *Mary Poppins* by P. L. Travers, London, Peter Davies, 1934, by permission of the Estate of the late P. L. Travers; book cover on p. 63 illustrated by Mary Shepard, *Mary Poppins*, HarperCollins Publishers Ltd, 2001, reprinted by permission of HarperCollins Publishers Ltd © (1934) P. L. Travers. Photographic representation of Katrice Horsley as Mary Poppins by permission of the Estate of the late P. L. Travers, and the Estate of Mary Shepard (represented by N. E. Middleton Artists' Agency).

Shirley Hughes & Clara Vulliamy: quotation on p. 64 and extract on p. 69 from Act 3 of *The Importance of Being Earnest* by Oscar Wilde, London, Leonard Smithers, 1889; photograph on p. 68, Lebrecht Music and Arts Photo Library/Alamy; photograph of Oscar Wilde on p. 69, Photos.com © Getty Images.

Terry Jones: quotation on p. 70, extract on p. 73 and book cover on p. 72 from *Rupert and King Frost* by Alfred Bestall in *Rupert Annual 1940,* London, Express Papers PLC, 1940. Rupert Bear is used with kind permission of DreamWorks Animation UK Ltd. Rupert Bear is a registered trademark of Classic Media Distribution Limited and Express Newspapers: all rights reserved. Thank you to Classic Media for permitting photographic representation of Terry Jones as Rupert Bear.

Geraldine McCaughrean: quotation on p. 74 and extract on pp. 78–9 from *Pride Comes Before a Fall: The Story of Bellerophon* © Geraldine McCaughrean, 2014; illustration on p. 79, Lebrecht Music and Arts Photo Library/Alamy.

Michael Morpurgo: quotation on p. 80 and extract on p. 83 from chapter 1 of *Great Expectations* by Charles Dickens, London, Chapman and Hall, 1860–61; illustration on p. 83 by F. W. Pailthorpe, *Great Expectations*, Robson and Kerslake, 1885; photograph of Charles Dickens on p. 83, Photos.com, © Getty Images.

Terry Pratchett: quotation on p. 84 and extract on p. 89 from chapters 6 & 1 of *Just William* by Richmal Crompton (© Richmal Crompton 1922), printed by permission of United Agents (www.unitedagents.co.uk) on behalf of Richmal Crompton Estate; illustration and book cover on p. 88 from *Just William* by Richmal Crompton as drawn by Thomas Henry Fisher, reprinted by permission of Peters Fraser and Dunlop (www.Petersfraserdunlop.com) on behalf of the Estate of Thomas Henry Fisher; photograph of Richmal Crompton on p. 89 © National Portrait Gallery, London. Photographic representation of Terry Pratchett as William Brown, used by permission of Macmillan's Children's Books, a division of Macmillan Publishers Ltd.

Philip Pullman: quotation on p. 90 and extract on p. 93 from chapters 8 & 10 of *Treasure Island* by Robert Louis Stevenson, London, Cassell & Co., 1883; illustration on p. 93 by Louis Rhead, *Treasure Island*, London, Harper Brothers, 1915.

Michael Rosen: Till Eulenspiegel cartoon strip on pp. 98–9, "Till Eulenspiegel and the Potentate's Portrait" © Neill Cameron, 2014.

Katherine Rundell: quotation on p. 100 and illustration and book cover on p. 103 from *Where the Wild Things Are* by Maurice Sendak, New York, Harper and Row, 1963, copyright © 1963 by Maurice Sendak, copyright renewed 1991 by Maurice Sendak, used by permission of HarperCollins Publishers. This selection may not be re-illustrated without written permission of HarperCollins. Photographic representation of Katherine Rundell as a Wild Thing from *Where the Wild Things Are* by Maurice Sendak. Copyright © Maurice Sendak, 1963, used by permission of The Wylie Agency (UK) Limited.

Holly Smale: quotation on p. 104 and extract on p. 107 from chapters 6 & 4 of *The Lion, the Witch and the Wardrobe* by C. S. Lewis, copyright © C. S. Lewis Pte Ltd. 1950, reprinted by permission; illustration on p. 106 and book cover on p. 107, *The Lion, the Witch and the Wardrobe* by C. S. Lewis, copyright © C. S. Lewis Pte Ltd. 1950, illustrations by Pauline Baynes © copyright C. S. Lewis Pte Ltd 1950, reprinted by permission.

Benjamin Zephaniah: quotation on p. 108 and story on pp. 112–13, "Anansi and the Basket of Stories" © Alex Kanefsky, 2014; illustration on p. 111 by Petrina Wright, from *The Illustrated Anansi* by Philip Sherlock, Oxford, Macmillan, 1995.

On p. 114; Spellbook belonging to Terry Pratchett, created by Rob Wilkins and Terry Pratchett.

On p. 117; Edward Lear, *Nonsense Songs and Stories*, Frederick Warne & Co, 1888; John Tenniel, *Alice's Adventures in Wonderland*, Macmillan & Co, 1865; Louis Rhead, *Treasure Island*, Harper Brothers, 1915; Charles Buchel, *Peter Pan* theatre poster, 1904, reprinted with kind permission of Great Ormond Street Children's Charity.